Directory of Grants for Organizations Serving People with Disabilities

Eleventh Edition

A Reference Directory Identifying Grants Available to Nonprofit Organizations

Research Grant Guides, Inc.
P.O. Box 1214
Loxahatchee, Florida 33470

Richard M. Eckstein
Publisher/Editor

Research and Administrative Staff:
Claire L. Eckstein
Lorraine Moynihan
Debra Reese

Marketing Representative:
CJ Marketing
Cathy J. Tosner
John P. Tosner

Printed in the U.S.A.

ISBN 0-945078-25-0

Table of Contents

Preface

To get started, use the *Directory* to research foundations that have previously awarded grants to your type of organization. You should review only the foundations listed within your own state. Be careful to remember that many funders limit grantmaking to their individual geographic areas. Geographic restrictions and grant range are listed when available to our research staff. Next, send a brief letter to the foundation to request a copy of their most recent grant guidelines. Guidelines issued by the funder should always be followed. Before writing a grant proposal, read the suggestions and strategies discussed in the "Introduction" and "Proposal Writing Basics."

Foundations may change their priorities and expenditure levels. Corporate foundations frequently respond to the general economy and may curtail their grantmaking programs until profits reach a satisfactory level. Don't be discouraged if your proposal is not funded on the first try.

Several elements in a successful grant proposal include:

1) Uniqueness of proposal subject matter

2) A clear, well-written application

3) A realistic budget

4) Qualifications of the Project Director

5) Issues of concern to the proposed sponsor

If the proposal warrants, there should be a table of contents to guide the reviewer. A timetable depicting your projected progress may also be helpful. Try to present a readable, professional-looking proposal written in clear language that avoids jargon.

Introduction

Research Grant Guides publishes specialized fund-raising directories. Each directory is an easy to use resource for identifying foundation sources of funding. This Directory, like the others in the series, includes all the information necessary to begin your funding search. This introduction will help you navigate the intricacies of locating just the right foundation sponsors to support your organization. It describes the step-by-step process through which ideas become funded grants. The introduction serves as a guide to the information in the Directory, and together they will help increase your likelihood of being awarded a grant.

What Are Grants?

Although this seems like an obvious question, it is important to understand exactly what a grant is and what it is not before proceeding with a search. It will also be useful to review the nature of foundations as a preface to discussing how to search for grant opportunities.

A grant is a mechanism through which one organization can influence the behavior of another. Grants generally are in the form of money, but they can also be made in the form of technical assistance or equipment. Grants serve as incentives to promote the interests and agenda of the foundation. The foundation awarding the grant is known as the grantor.

Organizations receiving grants are known as grantees. The foundation usually publishes guidelines explaining its interests and procedures for submitting an application or proposal. Any organization wishing to receive a grant should follow the guidelines. The applicant should describe itself and its needs in terms consistent with the foundation's interests.

Foundations generally receive many more applications than they can support. They will choose among them and make decisions based on how well the applicants can promote the foundation's own interests. The successful applicants will be those whose interests are the same or closely aligned with the foundation's and who can demonstrate that their organizations have the necessary experience and competence to carry out the work described in the proposal. Thus, successful applicants always understand the interests of the grantor and present their proposals in those terms. They also always speak with confidence and strength about their programs. Foundations support organizations capable of achieving success in their goals and who have the potential for making a positive impact on the lives of their constituents.

What Are Foundations?

There are several types of organizations calling themselves foundations. We are interested in foundations that award grants, or grantmaking foundations. Unless otherwise specified, when we use the term foundations in this introduction, we mean foundations to which nonprofit organizations may apply for grants.

Foundations can be created by individuals, families or companies interested in setting aside a sum of money to be used for awarding grants. The foundation generally invests the money in an endowment and makes grants from the earnings. In order for foundations to be able to devote as much money as possible for grants, they are not required to pay income taxes on their earnings.

Grants are considered to be in the public interest because they support the activities of tax-exempt nonprofit organizations. The U.S. Internal Revenue Service monitors foundations carefully to ensure that they award grants only to organizations declared tax-exempt. In order to be eligible to receive a grant, applicants must be able to document that their organizations meet all the qualifications listed under Section 501(c)(3) of the IRS Code. That is the section of the Code specifying the characteristics making an organization eligible for nonprofit status. Proper documentation is in the form of a letter from the IRS indicating to the organization that it has been designated tax-exempt under section 501(c)(3). That is the reason nonprofit organizations are also known as 501(c)(3) organizations.

The objective of using the directories in the Research Grant Guides' series is to identify the foundations most likely to support your organization. Foundations use grants to promote their own priorities by supporting the activities of nonprofit organizations. Some foundations may have very simple priorities. For example, they might consider any project within a specific community. Some may have extraordinarily specific priorities. An example would be a foundation interested in public or private schools, but not religiously affiliated schools, that provide special educational services to children with a specific disability. Thus, a special education program in a religious school would not be eligible, even though it does provide the type of service specified by the foundation. The possible combinations of priorities are almost endless.

Our research staff analyzes the records of thousands of foundations. We select those that are appropriate for inclusion in the Directory and condense their most important information into compact profiles in an easy to use format. The following is a step-by-step process for using our information to apply for and be awarded a grant.

Steps for Writing Proposals and Winning Grants

Step 1 - Understand Your Own Organization and its Needs

An absolutely essential part of the grant seeking process is to make sure you have a thorough understanding of your own organization, its priorities and its clients. This may sound obvious, but it is surprising how many staff members working in nonprofit organizations have never even seen the mission statement. Every grant seeker and proposal writer should have available from their organization its annual report, mission statement, accreditation reports and by-laws for reference. These should be reviewed periodically, especially when starting a new grant search.

Step 2 - Develop the Proposal Before Conducting Any Foundation Research

Next, it is equally important to have a clear understanding of the exact nature of the request to be made in the proposal. Planning the proposal/grant application must take place before undertaking any research because your job is to match your proposal with the specific requirements of the foundations you will apply to. The budget is especially important. Foundations vary widely with regard to the size of grants they award. The Directory reports typical grant ranges for most foundations. These ranges are the "comfort zone" for the foundations. Asking for too little money may be as detrimental as asking for too much. There are administrative costs associated with the grantmaking process, and some foundations may feel it is not cost effective to award grants below a certain amount. The "typical grant range" should be interpreted as a guide, not an inflexible standard.

This step is also important when deciding on how many proposals/applications to submit. It may turn out that no single foundation awards grants large enough to cover the entire project. It is perfectly acceptable to apply to several foundations and request grants for part of the budget. That's why it is so important to plan the proposal and determine its scope before doing anything else.

Step 3 - A Geography Lesson
The first thing the reader notices when examining the Directory is that it is subdivided by state. Generally, but not always, foundations tend to award grants close to their home base. They are said to "...give where they live...". Carefully reviewing all the entries for your home state is a good way to start using the Directory. This will provide an overview of foundations in your area.

It is important to make note of any within-state geographic preferences listed for the foundations in your state. This can work for or against you. Note any foundations that list a preference for specific areas. Any that specify your area should be at the top of your list of potential sponsors. Also make note of any within your state whose geographic preferences exclude your organization. Don't throw them out immediately, however. Your organization may be located in one part of the state, but may offer services beyond that immediate area. If that's the case, it is likely that your proposal will be eligible for consideration.

While reviewing the foundations in your state, pay careful attention to their interest areas. Highlight the names or place a check mark next to those whose interests match those of your organization. These will be your best prospects.

Most foundation profiles identify geographic restrictions. Where such information is unavailable, but the foundation is located in your state and specifies interests consistent with your own, send a letter as described in Step 6.

Step 4 - Identifying Specific Foundation Interests
This step presents an alternative method to that described in Step 3. This Directory includes only those foundations interested in the general subject specified in the title of the book. There are many sub-categories of priorities contained within the main subject. When researching foundations our goal is to identify those that are the closest fit. The subject index classifies foundations by interest area. It contains categories that correspond to all the possible priorities of the included foundations.

The foundations are numbered consecutively through the Directory. The first foundation listed under Alabama is number 1, and the last foundation in Wyoming has the highest number. The purpose of these numbers is to facilitate the research process. Make note of the range of foundation entry numbers for your state.

Under each category in the subject index are the entry numbers of all foundations expressing interest in that category. Keep in mind that the activities of your organization may correspond to several categories. Review all that apply to you. Make note of the entries corresponding to foundations that are within your state and that are also under the subject headings appropriate to your search. Eliminate any of these that you identified as having geographic restrictions excluding your region. After completing this step, you may have a lengthy list of entry numbers, which correspond to foundation names.

Step 5 - Narrowing the Search

Just because the foundations on your list match your organization's priorities, however, does not guarantee them to be the very best prospects. You have some more work to do to reduce your list to only the best potential sources. Your next step, therefore, is to review carefully the foundation profile in the Directory for each of the entry numbers on your list. You know from what you have already done that the foundations have an interest in the priority area that concerns you and that they support organizations in your geographic area. What else can you learn about them? A few additional questions will deepen your insight into these sources.

Are they interested in your type of organization? Most of the entries in the Directory list organizations to whom the foundations have made grants. Analyze this information, where available, to determine if any of these grantees are similar in purpose to your own.

1. Is this a community foundation? If so, the grants will be restricted to the geographic area specified in the name.

2. What is the typical grant size? Many of our foundation listings include the typical grant range. This range will tell you if the foundation will be likely to support the entire budget of your application. If not, you will need to apply to several so that your chances of receiving grant funds for the total budget will be greater.

3. Are they interested in the constituents you serve? Are there specific preferences, e.g. children, elderly, people with disabilities? Careful use of the subject index will reveal such preferences.

You must make sure the list includes all possible foundations whose priorities and interests match your own, but who don't exclude you geographically. Once you're satisfied that your list meets these criteria, it's time to start contacting the foundations on your list.

Step 6 - Making Contact with the Foundations

Once you have identified your list of potential foundations, you must next determine the best way to approach each one. Each foundation has its own way of dealing with potential applicants. It will not be productive to approach each in the same way or to develop an all-purpose proposal to send out. This is known as "shotgunning", and rarely results in success. Rather you, as the applicant, must research the procedures of each foundation and follow the instructions exactly.

One of the benefits of the directories from Research Grant Guides is that our staff has already eliminated those foundations that do not accept applications from the grant seeking public. Many small family foundations, for example, prefer to select grant applicants without receiving applications. They tend to support the same group of grantees year after year.

All the foundations listed in the Directory accept applications from nonprofit organizations. Many have specific requirements, while others ask only for a letter from the applicant describing the program for which it seeks support. You now need to contact the foundations themselves to see if they have any additional priorities and any specific procedures to be followed.

The applicant should write to each of the foundations on the list to request an application and any other materials that may be available. This should be in the form of a simple letter requesting their information. A good model would be, "This is to request a copy of your guidelines and any other application information you have available. Please send these to me at the following address." Address the letter, "Dear Foundation Director".

Don't try to describe your organization or the project, even briefly, at this point. The foundation may read such a description and decide to send a rejection letter on that basis alone. It happens frequently and precludes the applicant from submitting a formal proposal.

The scope of information you may receive will vary widely. Some foundations have nothing at all, while others have quite extensive and complex guidelines and procedures. If you do receive materials from the foundations, study the guidelines carefully and follow any instructions to the letter. If you receive nothing, send them a letter based on the outline in *Proposal Writing Basics* beginning on page 10.

What Else Can You Learn?

As noted previously, you will receive specific instructions from many of the foundations to whom you write for information. Some ask only for a letter. This letter, however, needs to include all the components of a typical grant proposal. It must include sections describing the applicant, the need for the grant, specific procedures, how much it will cost, what activities will be conducted, and how the project will be evaluated. Such letter applications should be limited to three single-spaced pages signed by the chief executive officer of the nonprofit organization.

Some foundations will accept common application forms. These grantors have grouped together within specific regions of the country and developed standard proposal formats acceptable to each member of the group. The common application forms are outlines indicating the proposal sections required by the members of the group. New York, Massachusetts, and California among others, have developed common grant application forms. Foundations that accept the common application form will let you know that they do in their response to your inquiry for information. The foundation may also include a copy of the form.

The valuable information contained in this Directory will help applicants prepare the most competitive grant applications. Good luck on your search.

Proposal Writing Basics

Despite the availability of excellent references on the subject, proposal writing still seems an elusive art. Many foundation grant officers despair at the poor quality of proposals they receive.

Proposals that fail to communicate effectively jeopardize the support that might be granted to an otherwise excellent project. Competition for funds is fierce. Many worthwhile projects must be declined because so many organizations pursue the limited dollars available. Poorly written proposals simply make it easy for the foundation to reject the request; there are too many good ones to consider. For the pressured foundation, it is impractical to spend time trying to make sense of unclear proposals.

Some Truths That Should Be Self-Evident

• Research, not writing, is the first step. Foundations have specific interests. These must be researched. Proposals should be submitted only to those sources that have articulated a priority in the type of project to be undertaken by the applicant. To do otherwise is like going shopping for groceries in a hardware store. The response can only be, "You're in the wrong place."

• Proposal writing requires a good writer. Communicating in clear, precise English assumes talent that not everyone possesses. Sometimes a proposal writer is in the wrong job. Although proposal writing is an excellent way to enter the fund-raising profession, it's not for everyone. Skills must be assessed accurately by the employer and job seeker. Writing is only one specialty required in fund-raising. People uncomfortable with writing can find many other rewarding career paths in professional fund-raising.

• Follow directions. Many foundations provide specific instructions on what they want in a submission. If such directions exist, they should be adhered to without deviation. Frequently, however, there are no specific guidelines. For such cases, the following outline provides a model of what should be contained in a proposal. The model is basic and flexible enough to accommodate different writing styles.

Starting: The Most Difficult Part

Questions that are asked frequently are: How should the proposal begin? and What is the best way to introduce the subject? The opening paragraph is of vital importance. It must set the stage and interest the reader enough to make him or her want to know more. All this in two or three sentences.

A most effective way to do this is to begin with a general or global statement of the problem to be addressed. Let's use the example of a project to provide neighborhood transportation for people with disabilities.

For example:

"The absence of accessible transportation constitutes a serious obstacle to people with disabilities in performing the routine tasks of everyday life."

This opening sentence would be followed by two or three other short statements. Their purpose is to focus the general issue to be addressed in the context of the local environment. These statements serve the purpose of describing how this issue manifests itself in the particular situation that is the subject of the proposal. The entire introduction should occupy no more than a half page of a three-page letter or a full page of a five-page formal proposal. Included might be some statistics descriptive of the severity of the problem and the population to be served.

Who Are You? Dealing From Strength

The second paragraph or section should describe the nonprofit organization proposing to conduct the project. The most important thing to remember here is not to assume any knowledge on the part of the reader. It is easy to become too familiar with an issue or organization. The effect on the proposal when this happens is an inadequate description. That's fatal to the case. The applicant must make sure the prospective foundation has a clear idea of precisely who is applying for the grant.

A good way to handle this section is to write several descriptions of the organization in advance. They should be of varying length. Taking time to do this results in a final description that presents the organization in its most favorable light.

That brings up another vital consideration. The nonprofit must convince the foundation that their proposal is the best way to conduct a project dealing with the subject issue. Using our example of a transportation program, the description should touch upon the following items:

- Knowledge of the client population
- Knowledge of the geographic area to be served
- Experience in providing the service proposed
- Familiarity with the issue
- Qualifications of the staff
- Acceptance in the community

If a nonprofit organization cannot present a compelling capability statement without exaggerating, it needs to evaluate its reasons for seeking funds for the project. Foundations strive to invest in organizations that have the ability to put grants to maximum use. This description of capabilities, therefore, is probably the most important information to be covered in a proposal.

How Much Will It Cost?

This is no place to be bashful. The amount of money requested should be indicated as early as possible in the proposal. Ideally it should be included in the first paragraph. The dollar request says a lot about the project. It establishes limits. It tells the foundation the extent of its participation. It says something about cost effectiveness. Finally, if the request is realistic, not too high or low for the foundation to whom it's directed, it tells the foundation that the applicant has done his or her homework.

What Will Be Different?

Until now you have been carefully setting the stage. You have prepared the reader to be interested in the project, which now must be described. What are the goals? How will it work? Who will benefit? Who will do the work? What will be accomplished?

In order for the description to be compelling, the project must have been well thought out. The heart of a good proposal is a good project. When the program has been well planned, this part of the proposal is easy to write. If that's not the case, the project planning must be reexamined. Often, project weaknesses become exposed in the act of attempting a written description that simply won't flow.

Other Considerations

Because writing styles are so individual, proposals will vary even if they are based on a common model. In all cases, the project itself will determine what is appropriate to include and omit. For example, a statement regarding how the organization will measure success is important. The formality and complexity of the evaluation design, however, will vary greatly.

Many foundations like to know whose company they are keeping. It's often useful to indicate what other sources of funding are going to be awarded for this project.

Finally, each organization has ancillary materials that can be appended to a proposal. A certificate of nonprofit status and an audited financial statement are standards. Other attachments should be included only if they make a contribution to the case.

In closing, it bears noting that proposal writing takes practice. It is a skill that requires development. This model provides a guide to the structure of a proposal. Substance and style are very much a function of the individual writer.

FOUNDATIONS

ALABAMA

1
Alabama Power Foundation, Inc.
17N-0011
P.O. Box 2641
Birmingham, AL 35291
(205) 257-2508

Helen Keller Eye Research Foundation; Alabama Eye Bank; Alabama Institute for Deaf and Blind Foundation, Inc.; Vivian B. Adams School for the Mentally Handicapped

Grants awarded to organizations located in Alabama.

Typical grant range: $2,000 to $50,000

2
The J.L. Bedsole Foundation
P.O. Box 1137
Mobile, AL 36633
(334) 432-3369

Physically and mentally disabled; hearing impaired; visually impaired; Alabama Special Camp for Children and Adults

Grants awarded to organizations located in Alabama, with an emphasis in the Mobile vicinity.

Typical grant range: $4,000 to $60,000

3
The Community Foundation of Greater Birmingham
2027 First Avenue North, Suite 410
Birmingham, AL 35203
(205) 328-8641

Alabama Institute for Deaf and Blind; United Cerebral Palsy (bus to assist people who are in wheelchairs); Service Guild Early Intervention Program (playground for children with special needs); Jefferson-Blount-St. Clair Mental Health/Mental Retardation Authority (helps people overcome mental illness); ARC (independent living residence for adults who are mentally retarded)

Grants awarded to organizations located in the Birmingham vicinity.

Typical grant range: $3,000 to $50,000

4
Hill Crest Foundation, Inc.
310 N. 19th Street
Bessemer, AL 35020
(205) 980-5888

Mental health; Mental Health Association

Grants awarded to organizations located in Alabama.

5
The Hugh Kaul Foundation
c/o AmSouth Bank of Alabama
P.O. Box 11426
Birmingham, AL 35202
(205) 326-4696

Glenwood Mental Health Services; ARC; The Exceptional Foundation

Grants awarded to organizations located in the Birmingham vicinity.

Typical grant range: $2,000 to $100,000

6

McWane Foundation
P.O. Box 43327
Birmingham, AL 35243
(205) 991-9888

Mental health; Cystic Fibrosis Society

Grants awarded to organizations located in Alabama.

Typical grant range: $1,000 to $15,000

7

Robert R. Meyer Foundation
c/o AmSouth Bank of Alabama
P.O. Box 11426
Birmingham, AL 35202
(205) 326-4696

National Multiple Sclerosis Society; The ARC of Jefferson County; United Cerebral Palsy; Glenwood Mental Health Services; Very Special Arts

Grants awarded to organizations located in the Birmingham vicinity.

8

Henry G. Sims & Henry U. Sims Memorial Fund
c/o AmSouth Bank of Alabama
P.O. Box 11426
Birmingham, AL 35202
(205) 326-5382

Visually impaired; Alabama Eye Bank; Birmingham Ear Institute

Grants awarded to organizations located in Alabama.

Typical grant range: $1,000 to $5,000

9

Susan Mott Webb Charitable Trust
c/o AmSouth Bank of Alabama
P.O. Box 11426
Birmingham, AL 35202
(205) 326-5410

Glenwood Mental Health Services; National Multiple Sclerosis Society

Most grants awarded to organizations located in the Birmingham vicinity.

Typical grant range: $5,000 to $50,000

ALASKA

10

The Skaggs Foundation
P.O. Box 20510
Juneau, AK 99802
(907) 463-4843

Physically disabled; Special Olympics

Grants awarded to organizations located in Alaska.

Typical grant range: $1,000 to $10,000

ARIZONA

11

Arizona Community Foundation
2122 E. Highland Avenue, Suite 400
Phoenix, AZ 85016
(602) 381-1400

Special Olympics Arizona; Arizona Center for Disability Law; Multiple Sclerosis Society; Goodwill Industries of Central Arizona; Prevent Blindness America; Recording for the Blind and Dyslexic; Arizona State Schools for the Deaf and Blind

Grants awarded to organizations located in Arizona.

12

Community Foundation for Southern Arizona
6601 E. Grant Road, Suite 111
Tucson, AZ 85715
(520) 722-1707

Very Special Arts Arizona

Grants awarded to organizations located in Cochise, Pima, and Santa Cruz Counties.

13
The Flinn Foundation
1802 N. Central Avenue
Phoenix, AZ 85004-1506
(602) 274-9000

Mental health; physically disabled;
Mental Health Association of Arizona

Grants awarded to organizations located
in Arizona.

Typical grant range: $5,000 to $150,000

14
The Marshall Fund of Arizona
3295 N. Drinkwater Blvd.
Scottsdale, AZ 85251
(480) 941-5249

Marc Center (program to train young
adults who are mentally disabled to be
self-sufficient)

Typical grant range: $5,000 to $20,000

15
Margaret T. Morris Foundation
P.O. Box 592
Prescott, AZ 86302
(520) 445-4010

Physically disabled; residential center for
people who are disabled

Previous recipients of funding from this
foundation are eligible to apply for
another grant.

Grants awarded to organizations located
in Arizona.

Typical grant range: $2,000 to $35,000

16
**William L. & Ruth L. Pendleton
Memorial Fund**
c/o Firstar Metropolitan Bank & Trust
3800 N. Central
Phoenix, AZ 85012
(602) 241-5667

Special Olympics; Center for Blind and
Visually Impaired

Grants awarded to organizations located
in Arizona.

Typical grant range: $1,000 to $20,000

17
St. Luke's Charitable Health Trust
2999 N. 44th Street, Suite 530
Phoenix, AZ 85018
(602) 808-9600

Mental Health Association of Arizona;
Recording for the Blind and Dyslexic;
Special Olympics; Foundation for Blind
Children; Gompers Center for the
Handicapped (dental services); EAR
Foundation of Arizona (hearing screening
program for newborns); Listen, Inc.
(services for children who are hearing
impaired); Mentally Ill Kids in Distress
(computer); Arizona School for the Deaf
and Blind (hearing aids); United Cerebral
Palsy (therapeutic equipment for children
who are disabled)

18
The Elizabeth Read Taylor Foundation
250 North Meyer
Tucson, AZ 85701

Mentally and physically disabled;
Salpointe Catholic High School (rest room
accessibility project)

Grants awarded to organizations located
in Tucson.

Typical grant range: $1,000 to $10,000

19
Del E. Webb Foundation
P.O. Box 3350
Wickenburg, AZ 85358
(520) 684-7223

Physically disabled; visually impaired;
developmentally disabled

Typical grant range: $10,000 to $100,000

ARKANSAS

20
Charles A. Frueauff Foundation, Inc.
Three Financial Centre
900 S. Shakleford, Suite 300
Little Rock, AR 72211
(501) 219-1410

Physically disabled; visually impaired;
Recordings for the Blind; National Center
for Disability Services

Typical grant range: $10,000 to $50,000

21
**The John G. Leake Charitable
Foundation**
P.O. Box 251414
Little Rock, AR 72225
(501) 666-1885

Easter Seal Telethon; Arkansas School
for the Deaf; Music for the Handicapped;
American Amputee Foundation (summer
program); Youth Homes, Inc. (special
education school)

Grants awarded to organizations located
in Arkansas.

Typical grant range: $500 to $6,000

22
Wal-Mart Foundation
702 S.W. 8th Street
Bentonville, AR 72716
(501) 273-4000

Physically disabled; visually impaired;
Disabled American Veterans; Pony
Express Association of the Blind

Grants awarded to organizations located
in areas of company operations (Wal-Mart
Stores).

Typical grant range: $1,000 to $25,000

23
Windgate Charitable Foundation, Inc.
P.O. Box 826
Siloam Springs, AR 72761
(501) 524-9829

Visually impaired; physically disabled;
Association for the Blind

Typical grant range: $3,000 to $60,000

CALIFORNIA

24
The Thomas C. Ackerman Foundation
600 W. Broadway, Suite 2600
San Diego, CA 92101
(858) 699-5411

Visually impaired; mental health; Canine
Companions for Independence

Grants awarded to organizations located
in the San Diego vicinity.

Typical grant range: $2,500 to $12,000

25
The Ahmanson Foundation
9215 Wilshire Blvd.
Beverly Hills, CA 90210
(310) 278-0770

Mental Health Association; Research to
Prevent Blindness, Inc.; Blind Children's
Center, Inc. (resurface roof and relocate
air conditioning units); Home Ownership
for Personal Empowerment (renovate two
residences for people who are
developmentally disabled)

Grants awarded to organizations located
in southern California, with an emphasis
in the Los Angeles vicinity.

Typical grant range: $10,000 to $50,000

26
AirTouch Communications Foundation
One California Street, 17th Floor
San Francisco, CA 94111
(415) 658-2300

Foundation for the Junior Blind;
California Council of the Blind; La Jolla
Playhouse (provide access for people who
are visually or hearing impaired)

Grants awarded to organizations located
in areas of company operations, with an
emphasis in San Francisco.

27
Alliance Healthcare Foundation
9325 Skypark Court, Suite 350
San Diego, CA 92123
(858) 874-3788

Deaf Community Services; San Diego
Alliance for the Mentally Ill; University
of California, San Diego (Office for
Students with Disabilities)

Grants awarded to organizations located
in California, with an emphasis in San
Diego.

28
**The Amateur Athletic Foundation of
Los Angeles**
2141 W. Adams Blvd.
Los Angeles, CA 90018
(213) 730-9600

Physically disabled; recreation; Special
Olympics; California Handicapped Skiers
Foundation

Grants awarded to organizations located
in southern California.

Typical grant range: $5,000 to $50,000

29
Amgen Foundation, Inc.
One Amgen Center Drive
Thousand Oaks, CA 91320
(805) 447-1000

Physically disabled; visually impaired

Grants awarded to organizations located
in areas of company operations (Amgen,
Inc.), with an emphasis in Ventura County.

30
ARCO Foundation
515 S. Flower Street
Los Angeles, CA 90071
(213) 486-3342

Foundation for the Junior Blind; Goodwill
Industries (vocational training); Friends of
the California Governor's Committee for
Employment (program for youth who are
disabled)

Grants awarded to organizations located
in areas of company operations (Atlantic
Richfield Co.).

Typical grant range: $2,500 to $50,000

31
Atkinson Foundation
1100 Grundy Lane, Suite 140
San Bruno, CA 94066
(650) 876-0222

Physically and mentally disabled; Mental
Health Association (housing for the
homeless who are mentally disabled)

Grants awarded to organizations located
in San Mateo County.

Typical grant range: $2,000 to $12,000

32
The William C. Bannerman Foundation
9255 Sunset Blvd., Suite 400
West Hollywood, CA 90069
(310) 273-9933

Camp Paivika (summer camp for children
who are disabled); Thresholds (education
program for Psychiatric Rehabilitation
Center)

Grants awarded to organizations located
in the Los Angeles vicinity.

Typical grant range: $2,000 to $15,000

33
The Donald R. Barker Foundation, Inc.
P.O. Box 936
Rancho Mirage, CA 92270
(760) 324-2656

Shriner's Hospital for Crippled Children;
Braille Institution of America

Typical grant range: $2,000 to $15,000

34
The Lowell Berry Foundation
Four Orinda Way, Suite 140B
Orinda, CA 94563
(925) 254-1944

Center for the Education of the Infant
Deaf; Mt. Diablo Rehabilitation Center

Typical grant range: $500 to $30,000

35

Blue Oak Foundation
555 Portola Road
Portola Valley, CA 94028

Children's Tree House (field trip for students who are deaf)

Most grants awarded to organizations located in San Mateo and Santa Clara Counties.

Typical grant range: $1,000 to $10,000

36

The Bothin Foundation
P.O. Box 29906
San Francisco, CA 94129
(415) 561-6540

Marin Center for Independent Living; Center for Handicapped Children and Teenagers (medical equipment for children and teenagers with disabilities); Independent Living Resource Center (telephone/voice mail system for center serving people with disabilities); Oakes Children's Center (telephone system for agency serving children who are emotionally disturbed); Santa Barbara Mental Health Association (purchase a residential facility for women who are mentally ill); Pioneer Park Project (building funds for a wheelchair ramp); North Bay Rehabilitation Services (renovate rest rooms for clients who are disabled)

Typical grant range: $1,000 to $15,000

37

Fritz B. Burns Foundation
4001 W. Alameda Avenue, Suite 203
Burbank, CA 91505
(818) 840-8802

Visually impaired; physically disabled; Braille Institute

Most grants awarded to organizations located in the Los Angeles vicinity.

Typical grant range: $5,000 to $100,000

38

California Community Foundation
445 S. Figueroa Street, Suite 3400
Los Angeles, CA 90071
(213) 413-4130

Physically and mentally disabled; blind; ARC of Southeast Los Angeles; Braille Institute of America (Career Services Program); Helen Keller International (Child Sight Program)

Grants awarded to organizations located in Los Angeles County.

Typical grant range: $3,000 to $30,000

39

The California Endowment
21550 Oxnard Street, Suite 600
Woodland Hills, CA 91367
(818) 703-3311

Blind Children's Center; Catholic Charities (grant to assist the elderly and people who are disabled); Alliance for Technology Access (technology program for people who are disabled); Chrysalis (mental health counseling program); Center for Independent Living (program for people who are disabled including employment, health care, and independent living skills)

Grants awarded to organizations located in California.

40
The California Wellness Foundation
6320 Canoga Avenue, Suite 1700
Woodland Hills, CA 91367
(818) 593-6600

Mental Health Association; Interim, Inc. (mental health services to assist adults with psychiatric and substance abuse problems); Catholic Charities (mental health and substance abuse services for mothers of young children); Foundation Consortium (program to improve the mental health of children, youth and families); California State University (health education and fitness program for people who are disabled)

Grants awarded to organizations located in California.

Typical grant range: $15,000 to $75,000

41
Callaway Golf Company Foundation
2285 Rutherford Road
Carlsbad, CA 92008
(760) 930-8686

Mentally and physically disabled; education; Eye Bank; Cleveland Sight Center (promote golf program for people who are blind); San Diego Friends of Parks and Recreation (recreation program for people who are disabled); Child Abuse Prevention Foundation (screening program for developmental disabilities)

Most grants awarded to organizations located in San Diego County.

Typical grant range: $5,000 to $25,000

42
Chartwell Foundation
1999 Avenue of the Stars, Suite 3050
Los Angeles, CA 90067
(310) 556-7600

Research to Prevent Blindness; Multiple Sclerosis Society

Grants awarded to organizations located in California, with an emphasis in Los Angeles.

Typical grant range: $5,000 to $100,000

43
The Codding Foundation
P.O. Box 6655
Santa Rosa, CA 95406
(707) 584-7550

Special Olympics; Community Resources for Independence

Grants awarded to organizations located in Sonoma County.

Typical grant range: $200 to $5,000

44
Crail-Johnson Foundation
222 W. Sixth Street, Suite 1010
San Pedro, CA 90731
(310) 519-7413

Mental Health Association; Association for Retarded Citizens; Foundation for the Junior Blind; Fries Avenue Elementary School (grant for a school psychiatric social worker); Holy Family Services Adoption and Foster Care (grant for a special needs and older children placement program)

Grants awarded to organizations located in the Los Angeles vicinity.

Typical grant range: $500 to $25,000

45
Carrie Estelle Doheny Foundation
707 Wilshire Boulevard, Suite 4960
Los Angeles, CA 90017-3501
(213) 488-1122

Recordings for the Blind; Blind Children's Center; Braille Institute; Doheny Eye Institute; Easter Seal Society; House Ear Institute; Crippled Children's Society

Most grants awarded to organizations located in the Los Angeles vicinity.

Typical grant range: $2,500 to $50,000

46
Joseph Drown Foundation
1999 Avenue of the Stars, Suite 1930
Los Angeles, CA 90067
(310) 277-4488

Visually impaired; Center for the Partially Sighted; Guide Dogs for the Blind

Grants awarded to organizations located in California.

Typical grant range: $10,000 to $50,000

47
The East Bay Community Foundation
501 Wickson Avenue
Oakland, CA 94610
(510) 836-3223

Physically disabled; Maya's Music Therapy Fund (program for adults who are developmentally disabled)

Grants awarded to organizations located in Alameda and Contra Costa Counties.

48
Exchange Bank Foundation
c/o Exchange Bank
P.O. Box 403
Santa Rosa, CA 95402
(707) 545-6220

Blind; physically disabled; Earle Baum Center of the Blind

Grants awarded to organizations located in Sonoma County.

Typical grant range: $1,000 to $6,000

49
Forest Lawn Foundation
1712 S. Glendale Avenue
Glendale, CA 91205

Physically disabled; visually impaired; Goodwill Industries

Grants awarded to organizations located in Los Angeles and Orange Counties.

Typical grant range: $1,500 to $50,000

50
Friedman Family Foundation
PMB 719, 204 East Second Avenue
San Mateo, CA 94401
(650) 342-8750

Jobs Consortium (peer counseling for people who are disabled and job preparation workshops); World Institute on Disability (discuss causes of high unemployment and poverty of people with disabilities)

Most grants awarded to organizations located in the San Francisco vicinity.

51
Georges and Germaine Fusenot Charity Foundation
590 N. Rossmore Avenue, Suite 10
Los Angeles, CA 90004
(323) 462-7702

Visually impaired; Foundation for the Junior Blind

Grants awarded to organizations located in California.

Typical grant range: $1,000 to $5,000

52
Gallo Foundation
P.O. Box 1130
Modesto, CA 95353
(209) 341-3204

Physically disabled; employment project

Most grants awarded to organizations located in California.

Typical grant range: $3,000 to $25,000

53
John Jewett and H. Chandler Garland Foundation
P.O. Box 550
Pasadena, CA 91102

Visually impaired; physically disabled; Guide Dogs for the Blind

Most grants awarded to organizations located in Southern California.

Typical grant range: $10,000 to $50,000

54
The Carl Gellert and Celia Berta Gellert Foundation
1169 Market Street, Suite 808
San Francisco, CA 94103
(415) 255-2829

Peninsula Association for Retarded Children and Adults; Blind Babies Foundation; Canine Companions for Independence; Hearing Society for the Bay Area; Lighthouse for the Blind; Peninsula Oral School for the Deaf; Recreation Center for the Handicapped, Inc.

Grants awarded to organizations located in the following counties: Alameda, Contra Costa, Marin, Napa, San Francisco, San Mateo, Santa Clara, Solano and Sonoma.

Typical grant range: $1,500 to $11,000

55
The Fred Gellert Family Foundation
361 3rd Street, Suite A
San Rafael, CA 94901-3580
(415) 256-5433

Physically disabled; visually impaired; Research Center for the Handicapped; Blind Babies Foundation; National Association for Visually Handicapped; Lighthouse for the Blind; Goodwill Industries, Inc. (job training program)

Grants awarded to organizations located in San Francisco, San Mateo, and Marin Counties.

Typical grant range: $2,000 to $20,000

56
Wallace Alexander Gerbode Foundation
470 Columbus Avenue, Suite 209
San Francisco, CA 94133
(415) 391-0911

Disability Rights Education and Defense Fund; Dole Foundation (employment project for people who are disabled)

Typical grant range: $5,000 to $50,000

57
Richard and Rhoda Goldman Fund
One Lombard Street, Suite 303
San Francisco, CA 94111
(415) 788-1090

Hearing impaired; visually impaired; Special Olympics

Grants awarded to organizations located in the San Francisco vicinity.

Typical grant range: $2,000 to $100,000

58
The Grousbeck Family Foundation
c/o Stanford University
Graduate School of Business, Room L-336
Stanford, CA 94305

Visually impaired; physically disabled; Perkins School for the Blind

Typical grant range: $10,000 to $75,000

59
Henry L. Guenther Foundation
2029 Century Park E., Suite 4392
Los Angeles, CA 90067
(310) 785-0658

Visually impaired; hearing impaired; Foundation for the Junior Blind

Most grants awarded to organizations located in Los Angeles.

Typical grant range: $5,000 to $100,000

60
Evelyn and Walter Haas, Jr. Fund
One Lombard Street, Suite 305
San Francisco, CA 94111
(415) 398-3744

Physically disabled; Christmas in April (home repair program for people who are disabled); Center for Independent Living (services for people who are disabled)

Grants awarded to organizations located in San Francisco and Alameda Counties.

Typical grant range: $3,000 to $35,000

61
Walter and Elise Haas Fund
One Lombard Street, Suite 305
San Francisco, CA 94111
(415) 398-4474

Mental Health Association; March of
Dimes; San Francisco Hearing and Speech
Center

Grants awarded to organizations located
in the San Francisco Bay vicinity.

Typical grant range: $3,000 to $50,000

62
The Luke B. Hancock Foundation
360 Bryant Street
Palo Alto, CA 94301
(650) 321-5536

Christian Blind Mission International;
Parents Helping Parents (program for
special needs children with mental,
physical, emotional or a learning
disability); Outreach (program to assist
people who are disabled and the elderly
in obtaining benefits and services);
San Mateo County Office of Education
(counseling program to serve families
with students who are emotionally
disturbed)

Grants awarded to organizations located
in the San Francisco vicinity.

Typical grant range: $5,000 to $50,000

63
Harden Foundation
P.O. Box 779
Salinas, CA 93902
(831) 442-3005

Emotionally disturbed; Multiple Sclerosis
Community Services; Meals on Wheels
(home meal delivery for clients who are
disabled); Animal Welfare Information
and Assistance (veterinary care for pets
owned by clients who are disabled and
elderly); Blind Babies Foundation
(child development services for infants
and preschool children who are visually
impaired); Valley Advocacy and
Communication Center (services for
people who are hearing-impaired)

Grants awarded to organizations located
in the Salinas vicinity.

Typical grant range: $5,000 to $40,000

64
The Humboldt Area Foundation
P.O. Box 99
Bayside, CA 95524
(707) 442-2993

Physically and mentally disabled; blind;
Northern Humboldt Eyes for the Blind;
Very Special Arts; Humboldt County
Special Olympics; Redwood Community
Action Agency (temporary wheelchair
ramp); Friends of Rio Del Library
(wheelchair accessibility project)

Grants awarded to organizations located
in Del Norte, Humboldt, Siskiyou, and
Trinity Counties.

Typical grant range: $1,000 to $50,000

65
Jaquelin Hume Foundation
600 Montgomery Street, Suite 2800
San Francisco, CA 94111
(415) 705-5115

Visually impaired; physically disabled;
Guide Dogs for the Blind

Grants awarded to organizations located
in the San Francisco vicinity.

Typical grant range: $2,000 to $50,000

66
Irvine Health Foundation
18301 Von Karman Avenue, Suite 440
Irvine, CA 92612
(949) 253-2959

Learning disabled; California State
University (Center for Children Who
Stutter)

Grants awarded to organizations located
in Orange County.

67
The James Irvine Foundation
One Market Street
Spear Tower, Suite 1715
San Francisco, CA 94105
(415) 777-2244

Physically disabled; Goodwill Industries

Most grants awarded to organizations
located in California.

Typical grant range: $20,000 to $100,000

68
George Frederick Jewett Foundation
The Russ Building
235 Montgomery Street, Suite 612
San Francisco, CA 94104
(415) 421-1351

Physically disabled; visually impaired;
School and Neuromuscular Center
(services for children who are
developmentally challenged); Meals on
Wheels (program that serves the elderly
and people who are disabled)

Typical grant range: $2,000 to $25,000

69
The Fletcher Jones Foundation
624 S. Grand Avenue, Suite 2900
Los Angeles, CA 90017
(213) 689-9292

John Tracy Clinic (screening program to
test hearing ability)

Grants awarded to organizations located
in California.

Typical grant range: $10,000 to $150,000

70
W.M. Keck Foundation
550 S. Hope Street, Suite 2500
Los Angeles, CA 90071
(213) 680-3833

Mental Health Association; United
Cerebral Palsy (facility for adults who are
developmentally disabled); Alliance for
Children's Rights (special education
program for children with a learning
disability); Vista Del Mar Child and
Family Services (care facility for children
who are mentally ill)

Typical grant range: $75,000 to $600,000

71
The Karl Kirchgessner Foundation
c/o Greenberg, Glusker, Fields, Claman &
Machtinger, L.L.P.
1900 Avenue of the Stars, Suite 2100
Los Angeles, CA 90067
(310) 553-3610

Recording for the Blind and Dyslexic;
San Diego Center for the Blind; Vista
Nova Home for the Blind; Blind Babies
Foundation; The Blind Children's
Learning Center; Visually Handicapped
Adults of the Valley; Canine Companions
for Independence; Braille Institute of
America, Inc.

Grants awarded to organizations located
in southern California.

Typical grant range: $5,000 to $40,000

72
Koret Foundation
33 New Montgomery Street, Suite 1090
San Francisco, CA 94105
(415) 882-7740

Visually impaired; physically disabled

Typical grant range: $5,000 to $75,000

73

Herbert & Gertrude Latkin Charitable Foundation
c/o Santa Barbara Bank and Trust
P.O. Box 2340
Santa Barbara, CA 93120
(805) 899-8407

National Multiple Sclerosis Society

Grants awarded to organizations located in the Santa Barbara vicinity.

Typical grant range: $3,000 to $10,000

74

Thomas and Dorothy Leavey Foundation
4680 Wilshire Blvd.
Los Angeles, CA 90010
(323) 930-4252

Visually impaired; mentally disabled; Foundation for the Junior Blind

Grants awarded to organizations located in southern California.

Typical grant range: $10,000 to $125,000

75

Lincy Foundation
150 S. Rodeo Drive, Suite 250
Beverly Hills, CA 90212

Mentally and physically disabled; visually impaired; Goodwill Industries

Most grants awarded to organizations located in California.

Typical grant range: $20,000 to $100,000

76

Miranda Lux Foundation
57 Post Street, Suite 510
San Francisco, CA 94104
(415) 981-2966

Physically disabled; Careers Abound (employment program for youth who are disabled)

Grants awarded to organizations located in San Francisco.

Typical grant range: $2,000 to $20,000

77

The Lyda-Rico DeLuca Foundation, Inc.
832 Barron Avenue
Redwood City, CA 94063
(650) 839-6527

Physically disabled; Recreation Center for the Handicapped

Grants awarded to organizations located in California.

Typical grant range: $1,000 to $15,000

78

Bertha Russ Lytel Foundation
P.O. Box 893
Ferndale, CA 95536

Physically disabled; accessibility project; Special Olympics; Easter Seal Society

Grants awarded to organizations located in Humboldt County.

Typical grant range: $500 to $25,000

79

Margoes Foundation
57 Post Street, Suite 510
San Francisco, CA 94104
(415) 981-2966

Mental health; physically disabled; developmentally disabled; cultural organizations; youth; Easter Seal Society; Progress Foundation (aftercare services for single mothers with psychiatric disabilities)

Grants awarded to organizations located in the San Francisco vicinity.

Typical grant range: $2,000 to $15,000

80

B.C. McCabe Foundation
8152 Painter Avenue, Suite 201
Whittier, CA 90602
(562) 696-1433

Visually impaired; Intercommunity Blind Center

Typical grant range: $10,000 to $100,000

81

The McConnell Foundation
P.O. Box 492050
Redding, CA 96049
(530) 226-6200

Physically disabled; visually impaired

Grants awarded to organizations located
in Shasta and Siskiyou Counties.

Typical grant range: $3,000 to $60,000

82

McKessonHBOC Foundation, Inc.
One Post Street, 31st Floor
San Francisco, CA 94104
(415) 983-8673

Mentally and physically disabled; Special
Olympics

Grants awarded to organizations located
in the San Francisco vicinity.

Typical grant range: $5,000 to $25,000

83

The Milken Family Foundation
1250 Fourth Street, 6th Floor
Santa Monica, CA 90401
(310) 998-2800

Visually impaired; physically disabled;
Center for the Partially Sighted

Most grants awarded to organizations
located in the Los Angeles vicinity.

Typical grant range: $2,000 to $65,000

84

Montgomery Street Foundation
235 Montgomery Street, Suite 1107
San Francisco, CA 94104
(415) 398-0600

Physically disabled; visually impaired;
learning disabled; Recreation Center for
the Handicapped; Center for the Partially
Sighted

Most grants awarded to organizations
located in California.

Typical grant range: $7,500 to $25,000

85

The Kenneth T. and Eileen L. Norris Foundation
11 Golden Shore, Suite 450
Long Beach, CA 90802
(562) 435-8444

Physically disabled; visually impaired;
youth; Blind Children's Center

Grants awarded to organizations located
in Los Angeles County.

Typical grant range: $5,000 to $80,000

86

Orange County Community Foundation
2081 Business Center Drive, Suite 100
Irvine, CA 92612
(949) 553-4202

Blind Children's Learning Center; Mental
Health Association (substance abuse
counselor for people who are mentally ill
and the homeless); Campfire Boys &
Girls (teach teenagers how to care for
children with special needs); Dayle
McIntosh Center (literacy training
program for individuals who are deaf)

Grants awarded to organizations located
in Orange County.

Typical grant range: $2,500 to $15,000

87

Pacific Life Foundation
700 Newport Center Drive
Newport Beach, CA 92660
(949) 640-3787

Providence Speech and Hearing Center;
Braille Institute; Very Special Arts;
National Multiple Sclerosis Society

Typical grant range: $2,500 to $10,000

88

The David and Lucile Packard Foundation
300 Second Street, Suite 200
Los Altos, CA 94022
(650) 948-7658

California Institute for Mental Health; Community Legal Services (education and advocacy project to maintain Supplemental Security Income benefits for children who are disabled); Chronicle Season of Sharing Fund (food, housing assistance and emergency needs for the clients who are disabled and elderly); Community Association for Rehabilitation (water therapy program for people who are developmentally disabled); United Fund (recreational activities for people with disabilities); Self-Help for Hard-of-Hearing People (mentoring program for children who are hard-of-hearing and their parents)

Most grants awarded to organizations located in Monterey, San Mateo, Santa Clara, and Santa Cruz Counties.

Typical grant range: $20,000 to $100,000

89

George B. Page Foundation
P.O. Box 1299
Santa Barbara, CA 93102
(805) 963-1841

Mentally disabled; dyslexia; Special Olympics

Grants awarded to organizations located in Santa Barbara.

Typical grant range: $3,000 to $25,000

90

The Parker Foundation
4365 Executive Drive, Suite 1600
San Diego, CA 92121
(858) 677-1431

Visually impaired; physically disabled; Canine Companions for Independence

Grants awarded to organizations located in San Diego County.

Typical grant range: $2,000 to $25,000

91

The Ralph M. Parsons Foundation
1055 Wilshire Blvd., Suite 1701
Los Angeles, CA 90017
(213) 482-3185

Institute for the Redesign of Learning (program serving children who are emotionally disabled); The Children's Nature Institute (science and nature experiences for children who are disabled); Crippled Children's Society (community service center for clients who are disabled); Violence Intervention Program (mental health services); Pasadena Scottish Rite Childhood Learning Disorders Center (diagnose and treat children with language disabilities); Valley Family Center (an after-school education program for children with learning disabilities); Deaf West (theater program with performances and classes for school children who are deaf)

Most grants awarded to organizations located in Los Angeles County.

Typical grant range: $15,000 to $80,000

92

Peninsula Community Foundation
1700 S. El Camino Real, Suite 300
San Mateo, CA 94402
(650) 358-9369

Mental Health Association; Blind Babies Foundation; Center for Independence of the Disabled; Jean Weingarten Peninsula Oral School for the Deaf (bilingual Spanish-English program for students who are deaf); College of San Mateo (employment program for adults who are disabled); Daly City Youth Health Center (mental health counseling services); Christmas in April (home repair program for people who are disabled); Mid-Peninsula Housing Coalition (housing program for adults with chronic mental illness)

Typical grant range: $15,000 to $30,000

93
Pfaffinger Foundation
Times Mirror Square
Los Angeles, CA 90053
(213) 237-5743

Physically disabled; visually impaired;
Easter Seal Society

Grants awarded to organizations located
in Los Angeles and Orange Counties.

Typical grant range: $5,000 to $35,000

94
The Riordan Foundation
300 S. Grand Avenue, 29th Floor
Los Angeles, CA 90071
(213) 229-8402

Visually impaired; physically disabled;
Helen Keller International (Child Sight
program)

Most grants awarded to organizations
located in California.

Typical grant range: $2,000 to $10,000

95
The Roberts Foundation
P.O. Box 29906
San Francisco, CA 94110

Mental health; learning disabled; Mental
Health Association

Typical grant range: $5,000 to $50,000

96
The San Francisco Foundation
225 Bush Street, Suite 500
San Francisco, CA 94104
(415) 733-8500

St. Joseph's Center for the Deaf and Hard
of Hearing; Disabled Women's Alliance;
San Francisco Network of Mental Health
Clinics; Prevent Blindness (vision
screening program); Bay Area Outreach
Recreation Program (recreation program
for youth who are disabled); Computer
Technologies Program, Inc. (program to
help people who are disabled become self-
sufficient); Lincoln Child Center (school-
based mental health prevention program)

Grants awarded in Alameda, Contra
Costa, Marin, San Francisco, and San
Mateo Counties.

Typical grant range: $2,000 to $60,000

97
Santa Barbara Foundation
15 E. Carrillo Street
Santa Barbara, CA 93101
(805) 963-1873

Physically and mentally disabled; visually
impaired; United Cerebral Palsy (apartment
complex for individuals who are disabled);
Family Service Agency (Latino Community
Mental Health Project)

Grants awarded to organizations located
in Santa Barbara County.

Typical grant range: $2,000 to $40,000

98
Frances Schermer Charitable Trust
c/o City National Bank
400 N. Roxbury Drive, 6th Floor
Beverly Hills, CA 90210
(310) 888-6324

Visually impaired; physically disabled;
emotionally disturbed; Braille Institute;
The Foundation for the Junior Blind

Typical grant range: $500 to $9,000

99
Sierra Health Foundation
1321 Garden Highway
Sacramento, CA 95833
(916) 922-4755

Mental health; physically disabled; youth; visually impaired; California Institute for Mental Health; Multiple Sclerosis Society

Typical grant range: $10,000 to $50,000

100
The May and Stanley Smith Trust
720 Market Street, Suite 250
San Francisco, CA 94102
(415) 391-0292

Foundation for the Junior Blind; Variety Club-Blind Babies Foundation (services for children who are blind); Audio Vision Radio Reading Service for the Blind (equipment); Center for the Education of Infant Deaf (speech development program for infants and toddlers who are deaf); North California Society to Prevent Blindness (school vision screening program)

Most grants awarded to organizations located in the San Francisco vicinity.

Typical grant range: $1,000 to $6,000

101
Sobrato Family Foundation
10600 N. De Anza Boulevard, Suite 200
Cupertino, CA 95014
(408) 446-0700

Jean Weingarten Peninsula Oral School for the Deaf; Parents Helping Parents, Inc. (education program for children with special needs); Alliance for Community Care (salary of mental health professional); Stanbridge Academy (program for children who are disabled)

Typical grant range: $5,000 to $30,000

102
Edward L. & Addie M. Soule Foundation
1840 San Miguel Drive, No. 202
Walnut Creek, CA 94596
(925) 935-3101

Guide Dogs for the Blind; Goodwill Industries; United Cerebral Palsy

Most grants awarded to organizations located in California.

103
The Harry and Grace Steele Foundation
441 Old Newport Blvd., Suite 301
Newport Beach, CA 92663
(949) 631-0418

Foundation for the Junior Blind; San Diego Center for the Blind; Canine Companions; Goodwill Industries

Grants awarded to organizations located in Orange County.

Typical grant range: $10,000 to $200,000

104
Glen and Dorothy Stillwell Charitable Trust
301 N. Lake Avenue, 10th Floor
Pasadena, CA 91101
(626) 793-9400

Physically disabled; visually impaired; youth; mental health; Orange County Performing Arts Center (program for people who are disabled); Pilgrimage Family Therapy (mental health program for low income families)

Grants awarded to organizations located in Orange County.

Typical grant range: $5,000 to $12,000

105
The Morris Stulsaft Foundation
100 Bush Street, Suite 825
San Francisco, CA 94104
(415) 986-7117

Lighthouse for the Blind and Visually Impaired; Jean Weingarten Peninsula Oral School for the Deaf; United Cerebral Palsy Association; Opportunity for Independence (van to transport people who are developmentally disabled); Community Alliance for Special Education (services for children with learning disabilities from low income families); Children's Learning Center (provide computers to students with learning disabilities); Hearing Society (program for children who are hearing impaired); Exodus, Inc. (group home for children who are autistic); Peninsula Association for Retarded Children and Adults (after school care); Recreation Center for the Handicapped (renovate rest rooms)

Grants awarded to organizations located in the San Francisco vicinity.

Typical grant range: $3,000 to $15,000

106
Swift Memorial Health Care Foundation
1317 Del Norte Road, Suite 150
Camarillo, CA 93010
(805) 988-0196

Visually impaired; physically disabled; Vision Loss Support Services

Grants awarded to organizations located in Ventura County.

Typical grant range: $1,000 to $5,000

107
S. Mark Taper Foundation
12011 San Vincente Blvd., Suite 400
Los Angeles, CA 90049
(310) 476-5413

Hearing impaired; visually impaired; physically disabled; independent living program

Most grants awarded to organizations located in California.

108
Thagard Foundation
215 E. Commonwealth Avenue, Suite A
Fullerton, CA 92832
(714) 738-7349

Shriners Hospital for Crippled Children

Most grants awarded to organizations located in California.

109
Alice Tweed Tuohy Foundation
205 E. Carrillo Street, Room 219
Santa Barbara, CA 93101
(805) 962-6430

Santa Barbara Special Olympics; Mental Health Association, Inc.; Santa Barbara Mental Health Association (grant for office furniture and computers)

Grants awarded to organizations located in the Santa Barbara vicinity.

Typical grant range: $1,000 to $25,000

110
The Upjohn California Fund
P.O. Box 90
Carmel Valley, CA 93924

Physically disabled; Easter Seal Society

Typical grant range: $500 to $3,000

111
The Valley Foundation
16450 Los Gatos Blvd., Suite 210
Los Gatos, CA 95032
(408) 358-4545

Physically disabled; visually impaired;
youth; cultural programs; San Jose
Children's Musical Theater (musical for
children who are disabled); De Anza
College (equipment for students with
disabilities in Adaptive Physical
Education program)

Grants awarded to organizations located
in Santa Clara County.

Typical grant range: $15,000 to $75,000

112
**Ventura County Community
Foundation**
1317 Del Norte Road, Suite 150
Camarillo, CA 93010
(805) 988-0196

Child Abuse and Neglect (mental health
project); Conejo Valley Unified School
(purchase a walker for a child who is
disabled); Ventura Unified School District
(adaptive toys for children who are
disabled)

Grants awarded to organizations located
in Ventura County.

113
Weingart Foundation
1055 W. Seventh Street, Suite 3050
Los Angeles, CA 90017
(213) 688-7799

San Diego Center for the Blind;
Association for Retarded Citizens; Boy
Scouts (expand program for children who
are disabled); ARC (van to transport
people with disabilities); Tierra Del Sol
Center for the Handicapped Foundation
(arts facility for people who are physically
or mentally disabled)

Grants awarded to organizations located
in southern California.

Typical grant range: $5,000 to $125,000

114
Wood-Claeyssens Foundation
P.O. Box 30586
Santa Barbara, CA 93130
(805) 966-0543

Dyslexia Awareness and Resource Center;
Braille Institute; Recording for the Blind
and Dyslexic; Special Olympics; National
Multiple Sclerosis Society; Therapeutic
Riding Academy; Easter Seal Society;
United Cerebral Palsy

Most grants awarded to organizations
located in the following counties: Santa
Barbara and Ventura.

Typical grant range: $5,000 to $50,000

COLORADO

115
The Anschutz Family Foundation
555 17th Street, Suite 2400
Denver, CO 80202
(303) 293-2338

United States Association of Blind
Athletes; Colorado Center for the Blind;
Center for Hearing, Speech and
Language; Colorado Alliance for the
Mentally Ill; Colorado Cross Disability
Coalition; Colorado Therapeutic Riding
Center; Center for Independent Living;
International Hearing Dog; United
Cerebral Palsy Association; Columbine
Lakewood Soccer Association (program
for children with disabilities); Moffat
County Senior Citizens (accessible bus for
people who are disabled); Town of
Littleton Cares, Inc. (food program for
homebound, elderly and people who are
disabled)

Grants awarded to organizations located
in Colorado.

Typical grant range: $3,000 to $10,000

116
The Aspen Valley Community Foundation
110 East Hallam Street, Suite 126
Aspen, CO 81611
(970) 925-9300

Aspen Camp School for the Deaf (summer and winter programs for children who are hearing-impaired); Challenge Aspen (recreation programs for people who are disabled)

Grants awarded to organizations located in Pitkin, Garfield and West Eagle Counties.

117
Boettcher Foundation
600 17th Street, Suite 2210 South
Denver, CO 80202
(303) 534-1937

Physically disabled; hearing impaired; visually impaired; United Cerebral Palsy; Goodwill Industries; National Sports Center for the Disabled; Colorado Easter Seal Society (program for children who are disabled)

Grants awarded to organizations located in Colorado.

Typical grant range: $10,000 to $100,000

118
Bonfils-Stanton Foundation
1601 Arapahoe Street, Suite 5
Denver, CO 80202
(303) 825-3774

Mental Health Association; Easter Seal Society; Delta Gamma Anchor Center for Blind Children; Aspen Camp School for the Deaf; Recording for the Blind & Dyslexic, Inc.; International Hearing Dogs, Inc.; United Cerebral Palsy; Capitol Hill Action and Recreation Group (services for people with mental illness); Denver Children's Home (residential and outpatient treatment program for children who are emotionally disturbed); Havern Center, Inc. (education fund for children who are disabled); Laradon Hall Society for Exceptional Children and Adults (program for children who are developmentally disabled); MesAbility, Inc. (transportation services for people with disabilities); Wray Rehabilitation and Activities Center, Inc. (upgrade facility to meet the American Disability Act requirements)

Grants awarded to organizations located in Colorado.

Typical grant range: $2,000 to $30,000

119
Temple Hoyne Buell Foundation
1666 S. University Blvd., Suite B
Denver, CO 80210
(303) 744-1688

National Sports Center for the Disabled; Center for Hearing, Speech and Language; Jefferson Center for Mental Health; United Cerebral Palsy; The Federation of Families for Children's Mental Health

Most grants awarded to organizations located in Colorado, with an emphasis in Denver.

Typical grant range: $5,000 to $25,000

120
Nathan B. & Florence R. Burt Foundation
1600 Lincoln Street, Suite 2750
Denver, CO 80264
(303) 863-8400

Families for the Blind; Radio Reading; Center for Hearing Impaired

Grants awarded to organizations located in Colorado.

121
The Christian Foundation
P.O. Box 457
Louisville, CO 80027

Therapeutic Riding Center (horseback riding program for people who are disabled); CHARG Resource Center (vocational training program for people who have a mental illness)

Most grants awarded to organizations located in Colorado.

Typical grant range: $2,500 to $10,000

122
Colorado Springs Community Trust Fund
P.O. Box 1443
Colorado Springs, CO 80901
(719) 389-1251

Pikes Peak Mental Health; Pikes Peak Partnership (vehicle to transport people who are physically disabled); Cheyenne Village (furniture for cabins used by adults who are developmentally disabled)

Most grants awarded to organizations located in Colorado, with an emphasis in El Paso County.

Typical grant range: $500 to $4,000

123
The Community Foundation Serving Northern Colorado
The Nicol Building
528 S. College
Fort Collins, CO 80524
(970) 224-3462

Physically disabled; Retired Seniors Volunteers Program (The Handyman Program: home repair and maintenance services for people who are disabled)

Grants awarded to organizations located in northern Colorado.

124
Comprecare Foundation, Inc.
1145 Bannock Street
Denver, CO 80204
(303) 832-1005

Pikes Peak Mental Health Center Systems, Inc.; Cheyenne Village, Inc. (horticultural therapy for clients who are developmentally disabled); Mt. Saint Vincent Home (services for children with severe emotional and behavioral difficulties); Colorado Mountain College (medical transportation services and education programs for people who are disabled)

Grants awarded to organizations located in Colorado.

Typical grant range: $3,000 to $15,000

125

Adolph Coors Foundation
3773 Cherry Creek North Drive, Suite 955
Denver, CO 80209
(303) 388-1636

National Sports Center for the Disabled;
Aspen Camp School for the Deaf; Mesa
Developmental Services (renovate group
home for agency serving people who are
developmentally disabled); Preserve
Sight-Colorado (preserve sight and
prevent blindness); Emily Griffith
Foundation (convert auditorium into a
high-tech satellite communication
instructional center that is accessible for
people who are disabled)

Grants awarded to organizations located
in Colorado.

Typical grant range: $5,000 to $80,000

126

The Denver Foundation
950 S. Cherry Street, Suite 220
Denver, CO 80246
(303) 300-1790

Recording for the Blind and Dyslexic;
Very Special Arts Colorado; Radio
Reading Service of the Rockies, Inc.;
Physically Handicapped Amateur Musical
Actors League, Inc.; International Hearing
Dog, Inc.; The Delta Gamma Anchor
Preschool for Blind Children; Aurora
Mental Health Center; Center for Hearing,
Speech and Language; Goodwill
Industries; The Legal Center for People
with Disabilities and Older People;
Colorado Foundation of Dentistry for the
Handicapped; National Sports Center for
the Disabled; United Cerebral Palsy;
Senior Support Services (Disabled
Homeless Seniors Housing Project); The
Children's Hospital Foundation (research
on the effectiveness of medication on
children who are mentally disabled)

Typical grant range: $5,000 to $25,000

127

John G. Duncan Trust
c/o Wells Fargo
P.O. Box 5825
Denver, CO 80217
(303) 293-5324

Hearing impaired; physically disabled;
International Hearing Dog

Grants awarded to organizations located
in Colorado.

Typical grant range: $2,500 to $10,000

128

El Pomar Foundation
Ten Lake Circle
Colorado Springs, CO 80906
(719) 633-7733

Physically disabled; education; youth;
recreation; Goodwill Industries; Colorado
School for the Deaf and Blind

Grants awarded to organizations located
in Colorado.

Typical grant range: $5,000 to $100,000

129

Gates Family Foundation
3200 Cherry Creek South Drive, Suite 630
Denver, CO 80209
(303) 722-1881

Physically disabled; hearing impaired;
education; Gathering Place (accessibility
project)

Most grants awarded to organizations
located in Colorado, with an emphasis in
the Denver vicinity.

Typical grant range: $5,000 to $90,000

130

Mabel Y. Hughes Charitable Trust
c/o Wells Fargo
P.O. Box 5825
Denver, CO 80217
(303) 293-5324

Physically disabled; National Sports
Center for the Disabled

Grants awarded to organizations located
in Colorado.

Typical grant range: $5,000 to $25,000

131
A.V. Hunter Trust, Inc.
650 S. Cherry Street, Suite 535
Denver, CO 80246
(303) 399-5450

Recording for the Blind and Dyslexic;
Anchor Center for Blind Children; United
Cerebral Palsy; Colorado Easter Seal
Society; Colorado Foundation of
Dentistry for the Handicapped (donated
dental services program); National Sports
Center for the Disabled (program for
winter and summer sports)

Most grants awarded to organizations
located in Denver.

Typical grant range: $2,000 to $30,000

132
JJJ Foundation, Inc.
287 Century Circle, Suite 100
Louisville, CO 80027
(303) 926-1111

ARC (program for children and adults
who are mentally or physically disabled);
Tiny Tim Developmental Preschool
(specialized learning program for children
with special needs); Colorado RUSH
(soccer program for children who are
physically disabled); Magnet School of
the Deaf (pilot program at new school for
children who are deaf); Colorado
Therapeutic Riding Center (horseback
riding therapy program for children who
are physically disabled)

Grants awarded to organizations located
in Colorado.

Typical grant range: $1,000 to $5,000

133
Helen K. and Arthur E. Johnson Foundation
1700 Broadway, Room 2302
Denver, CO 80290
(303) 861-4127

Easter Seal Society; Recording for the
Blind; Developmental Disabilities
Resource Center; International Hearing
Dog, Inc.; Anchor Center for Blind
Children (therapy programs); Disabled
Resource Services (youth employment
program); Society for Exceptional
Children (Community Adolescent
Transition Center)

Grants awarded to organizations located
in Colorado.

Typical grant range: $5,000 to $50,000

134
The Carl W. and Carrie Mae Joslyn Charitable Trust
Trust Department
P.O. Box 1699
Colorado Springs, CO 80942
(719) 227-6439

Physically disabled; visually impaired;
education

Grants awarded to organizations located
in El Paso County.

Typical grant range: $1,000 to $6,000

135
Kenneth Kendal King Foundation
900 Pennsylvania Street
Denver, CO 80203
(303) 832-3200

Visually impaired; physically disabled;
education; Goodwill Industries

Most grants awarded to organizations
located in the Denver vicinity.

Typical grant range: $1,000 to $35,000

136
Monfort Family Foundation
Box 890
Greeley, CO 80632
(970) 356-7529

March of Dimes; National Sports Center
for the Disabled

Grants awarded to organizations located
in Weld County.

Typical grant range: $1,000 to $25,000

137
The Aksel Nielsen Foundation
13115 N. Melody Lane
Parker, CO 80138
(303) 841-3581

Physically disabled; visually impaired;
recreation; National Sports Center for the
Disabled

138
The Summit Foundation
P.O. Box 4000
Breckenridge, CO 80424
(970) 453-5970

Physically disabled; Mental Health Center

Grants awarded to organizations located
in Summit County.

CONNECTICUT

139
The Beatrice Fox Auerbach Foundation
25 Brookside Blvd.
West Hartford, CT 06107
(860) 232-5854

Visually impaired; mentally disabled;
Fidelco Guide Dog Foundation

Most grants awarded to organizations
located in Connecticut, with an emphasis
in the Hartford vicinity.

Typical grant range: $3,000 to $60,000

140
The Barnes Foundation, Inc.
P.O. Box 315
East Hartland, CT 06027-0315
(860) 653-0462

Devereux Glenholme School
(horticultural program for students who
are emotionally disturbed); Forman
School (program for teachers with
students who are learning disabled)

Grants awarded to organizations located
in Connecticut.

141
**The Community Foundation of
Southeastern Connecticut**
P.O. Box 769
New London, CT 06320
(860) 442-3572

Physically disabled; cultural programs;
accessibility projects; youth; High Hopes
Therapeutic Riding Inc.; Garde Arts
Center (accessible elevator for people who
are disabled); Stonington Historical
Society (access ramp for library); Easter
Seals Rehabilitation Center (orthopedic
clinic); YMCA (accessible elevator for
people who are disabled)

Grants awarded to organizations located
in southeastern Connecticut.

142
**The Educational Foundation
of America**
35 Church Lane
Westport, CT 06880
(203) 226-6498

Learning disabled; physically disabled;
National Center for Learning Disabilities

Typical grant range: $10,000 to $100,000

143

Fairfield County Foundation, Inc.
523 Danbury Road, Route 7
Wilton, CT 06897
(203) 834-9393

Mid-Fairfield Child Guidance Center
(program for children who are
emotionally disturbed); Mid-Fairfield
Child Guidance Center (accessible van
for people who are disabled); YMCA
(accessibility project); Christian Day
School (mental health services); CLASP
Homes (services for individuals who are
mentally disabled)

Grants awarded to organizations located
in Fairfield County.

144

**The Greater Bridgeport Area
Foundation, Inc.**
940 Broad Street
Bridgeport, CT 06604
(203) 334-7511

Special Olympics; Connecticut
Association for Children with Learning
Disabilities

Grants awarded in the following
communities: Bridgeport, Easton,
Fairfield, Milford, Monroe, Shelton,
Stratford, Trumbull, and Westport.

Typical grant range: $100 to $20,000

145

Hartford Foundation for Public Giving
85 Gillett Street
Hartford, CT 06105
(860) 548-1888

Greater Hartford Association for Retarded
Citizens; Special Olympics; Hartford
Community Mental Health Center; United
Cerebral Palsy; Fidelco Guide Dog
Foundation, Inc.; Connecticut Institute for
the Blind; American School for the Deaf
(mobile hearing program); Connecticut
Union of Disability Action Groups (health
care program for people who are
disabled); Greater Hartford Transit
District (vans serving riders who are
disabled); Library Association of
Warehouse Point, Inc. (renovate library to
make it more accessible to people with
disabilities); Union School (building
funds for an accessible playground);
University of Connecticut Foundation
(accessible elevator for people who are
disabled)

Grants awarded to organizations located
in the Hartford vicinity.

Typical grant range: $15,000 to $75,000

146

**The Maximilian E. & Marion O.
Hoffman Foundation, Inc.**
970 Farmington Avenue, Suite 203
West Hartford, CT 06107
(860) 521-2949

Hearing impaired; physically and
mentally disabled; American School for
the Deaf

Typical grant range: $3,000 to $50,000

147

The Cyrus W. & Amy F. Jones & Bessie D. Phelps Foundation, Inc.
c/o Tellalian & Tellalian
211 State Street
Bridgeport, CT 06604
(203) 333-5566

Physically disabled; Goodwill Industries of Western Connecticut

Grants awarded to organizations located in Connecticut, with an emphasis in Bridgeport.

Typical grant range: $500 to $8,000

148

The Koopman Fund, Inc.
17 Brookside Blvd.
W. Hartford, CT 06107
(860) 232-6406

Hearing impaired; American School for the Deaf

Most grants awarded to organizations located in Connecticut.

Typical grant range: $100 to $3,000

149

McDonald Family Trust
c/o Tyler, Cooper & Alcorn
Cityplace, 35th Floor
Hartford, CT 06103
(860) 725-6200

Connecticut Institute for the Blind; Recording for the Blind and Dyslexic

Most grants awarded to organizations located in Hartford.

Typical grant range: $2,500 to $7,500

150

Emily Hall Tremaine Foundation, Inc.
290 Pratt Street
Meriden, CT 06450
(203) 639-5544

Learning Disabilities Association of America; National Center for Learning Disabilities

Typical grant range: $5,000 to $50,000

151

Union Carbide Foundation, Inc.
39 Old Ridgebury Road
Danbury, CT 06817
(203) 794-6945

Physically disabled; National Center for Disability Services

Grants awarded to organizations located in areas of company operations (Union Carbide Corporation).

Typical grant range: $3,000 to $25,000

152

The E. Matilda Ziegler Foundation for the Blind, Inc.
20 Thorndal Circle
Darien, CT 06820
(203) 356-9000

Visually impaired; Fidelco Guide Dog Foundation; Jadley School for the Blind

DELAWARE

153

Chichester duPont Foundation, Inc.
3120 Kennett Pike
Wilmington, DE 19807
(302) 658-5244

Physically disabled; youth; accessibility project

154

Crestlea Foundation, Inc.
100 W. 10th Street, Suite 1109
Wilmington, DE 19801
(302) 654-2489

Delaware Special Olympics

Grants awarded to organizations located in Delaware.

155
Crystal Trust
1088 DuPont Building
Wilmington, DE 19898
(302) 774-8421

Mentally and physically disabled; visually impaired; Alliance for the Mentally Ill

Grants awarded to organizations located in Delaware, with an emphasis in Wilmington.

Typical grant range: $5,000 to $75,000

156
Delaware Community Foundation
P.O. Box 1636
Wilmington, DE 19899
(302) 571-8004

Benedictine School (home for young adults who are developmentally disabled); Delaware Curative Workshop (rest rooms that are accessible); The ARC of Delaware (education program for parents who are mentally disabled); Delaware Early Childhood Center (program for children who are disabled)

Grants awarded to organizations located in Delaware.

Typical grant range: $2,000 to $20,000

157
Laffey-McHugh Foundation
1220 Market Building
P.O. Box 2207
Wilmington, DE 19899
(302) 658-9141

Mentally and physically disabled; visually impaired; education; Recording for the Blind and Dyslexic

Grants awarded to organizations located in Delaware, with an emphasis in Wilmington.

Typical grant range: $4,000 to $50,000

158
Longwood Foundation, Inc.
100 W. 10th Street, Suite 1109
Wilmington, DE 19801
(302) 654-2477

Mentally disabled; visually impaired; Delaware Foundation for Retarded Children

Grants awarded to organizations located in Delaware, with an emphasis in Wilmington.

Typical grant range: $50,000 to $300,000

159
Welfare Foundation, Inc.
100 W. 10th Street, Suite 1109
Wilmington, DE 19801
(302) 654-2489

Physically disabled; visually impaired; mental health; Association for the Blind

Grants awarded to organizations located in Delaware, with an emphasis in Wilmington.

Typical grant range: $5,000 to $75,000

DISTRICT OF COLUMBIA

160
The Morris and Gwendolyn Cafritz Foundation
1825 K Street, N.W., 14th Floor
Washington, DC 20006
(202) 223-3100

Goodwill Industries; Easter Seal Society for Disabled Children and Adults; Gallaudet University (Mental Health Center); City Lights School (education and therapy program for youth who are emotionally disturbed)

Grants awarded to organizations located in the Washington, DC vicinity.

Typical grant range: $10,000 to $100,000

161

The Lois & Richard England Family Foundation, Inc.
P.O. Box 11582
Washington, DC 20008
(202) 244-4636

Recording for the Blind and Dyslexic; Very Special Arts; Bazelon Center for Mental Health Law

Grants awarded to organizations located in the Washington, DC vicinity.

162

Fannie Mae Foundation
North Tower
4000 Wisconsin Avenue, N.W.
Washington, DC 20016
(202) 274-8000

National Organization on Disability; United Cerebral Palsy; National Multiple Sclerosis Society; Anchor Mental Health (group homes for people who are mentally ill); Independent Living for the Handicapped (special needs housing and services); District of Columbia Special Olympics (sports programs for adults and youth who are mentally or physically disabled); Foundation for Educational Innovation (job training for youth who are disabled); Lab School of Washington (program for children and adults with learning disabilities); Recording for the Blind and Dyslexic of Metropolitan Washington (services for students who are learning disabled)

Typical grant range: $5,000 to $35,000

163

John Edward Fowler Memorial Foundation
1725 K Street, N.W., Suite 1201
Washington, DC 20006
(202) 728-9080

Learning disabled; mental health; Multiple Sclerosis Society; Washington Very Special Arts

Grants awarded to organizations located in the Washington, DC vicinity.

Typical grant range: $4,000 to $20,000

164

The Freed Foundation
3050 K Street, N.W., Suite 220
Washington, DC 20007
(202) 337-5487

Washington Very Special Arts; The Seeing Eye; Gallaudet University

Grants awarded to organizations located in the Washington, DC vicinity.

Typical grant range: $2,000 to $35,000

165

The Philip L. Graham Fund
c/o The Washington Post Co.
1150 15th Street, N.W.
Washington, DC 20071
(202) 334-6640

Mental health; mentally disabled; Mental Health Association

Grants awarded to organizations located in the Washington, DC vicinity.

Typical grant range: $5,000 to $35,000

166

Jovid Foundation
5335 Wisconsin Avenue, N.W., Suite 440
Washington, DC 20015
(202) 686-2621

Physically disabled; mental health; Goodwill Industries

Most grants awarded to organizations located in Washington, DC.

Typical grant range: $2,000 to $10,000

167

Eugene and Agnes E. Meyer Foundation
1400 16th Street, N.W., Suite 360
Washington, DC 20036
(202) 483-8294

Mental health; physically disabled; visually impaired; education; Goodwill Industries; Very Special Arts

Grants awarded to organizations located in the Washington, DC vicinity.

Typical grant range: $12,000 to $35,000

168

Last minute update: The foundation originally listed here has terminated.

169

Public Welfare Foundation, Inc.
2600 Virginia Ave., N.W., Suite 505
Washington, DC 20037
(202) 965-1800

Recording for the Blind and Dyslexic; Union of Disability Action Groups; Mental Health Consumer Network; Cross-Disability Coalition; Bazelon Center for Mental Health Law; Resident Home for the Mentally Retarded; George Washington University Medical Center (Center for the Study and Advancement of Disability Policy)

Typical grant range: $20,000 to $75,000

FLORIDA

170

Ruth Anderson Foundation
2511 Ponce De Leon Blvd., Suite 320
Coral Gables, FL 33134
(305) 444-6121

Physically disabled; mental health; hearing impaired; speech impaired; March of Dimes; Hearing and Speech Center

Grants awarded to organizations located in the Miami vicinity.

Typical grant range: $500 to $8,000

171

Edyth Bush Charitable Foundation, Inc.
199 E. Welbourne Avenue
P.O. Box 1967
Winter Park, FL 32790
(407) 647-4322

United Cerebral Palsy; Association for Retarded Citizens; Florida Lions Conklin Center for Multihandicapped Blind; Center for Independent Living (services for young adults who are disabled)

Typical grant range: $10,000 to $60,000

172

The Chatlos Foundation, Inc.
P.O. Box 915048
Longwood, FL 32791
(407) 862-5077

Visually impaired; physically disabled; Foundation Fighting Blindness

Typical grant range: $3,000 to $30,000

173

Community Foundation for Palm Beach and Martin Counties, Inc.
324 Datura Street, Suite 340
West Palm Beach, FL 33401
(561) 659-6800

Palm Beach Habilitation Center; Autism Society of America; Department of Exceptional Student Education; Center for Group Counseling (mental health evaluation and counseling services for Head Start children); Meadow Park Elementary School (Prekindergarten Parent Involvement Project for parents of children who are disabled)

Grants awarded to organizations located in Palm Beach and Martin Counties.

Typical grant range: $1,000 to $15,000

174
Community Foundation of Central Florida, Inc.
P.O. Box 2071
Orlando, FL 32802
(407) 872-3050

Learning Disabilities Association

Grants awarded to organizations located in central Florida, with an emphasis in Orange, Osceola, and Seminole Counties.

175
Community Foundation of Collier County
2400 Tamiami Trail North, Suite 300
Naples, FL 34103
(941) 649-5000

WGCU-FM Radio Reading Service; Muscular Dystrophy Association; Alliance for the Mentally Ill

Grants awarded to organizations located in Collier County.

Typical grant range: $2,000 to $11,000

176
The Community Foundation of Sarasota County, Inc.
P.O. Box 49587
Sarasota, FL 34230
(941) 955-3000

Easter Seal Society; Special Olympics; Mental Health Community Centers, Inc.; Alliance for the Mentally Ill; Friends of Oscar Scherer Park, Inc. (accessible playground for people who are disabled); Lighthouse for the Blind, Inc. (independent living program for adults); Children's Haven and Adult Community Services, Inc. (renovate campus to meet the American Disabilities Act)

Grants awarded to organizations located in Sarasota County.

Typical grant range: $1,000 to $20,000

177
The Community Foundation of Tampa Bay
4950 W. Kennedy Blvd., Suite 250
Tampa, FL 33609
(813) 282-1975

Florida Special Olympics; March of Dimes; Muscular Dystrophy Association; Association for Retarded Citizens

Grants awarded to organizations located in the Tampa vicinity.

178
Dade Community Foundation, Inc.
200 S. Biscayne Blvd., Suite 2780
Miami, FL 33131
(305) 371-2711

Miami Museum of Science (program to bring wildlife to the homes and hospital rooms of children who are disabled); S.O.S. Respite Services (grant providing children and adults who are disabled with social and recreational programs); Zoological Society of Florida (program to adapt the curriculum to reach children with special needs)

Grants awarded to organizations located in Dade County.

Typical grant range: $1,000 to $20,000

179
Jessie Ball duPont Fund
225 Water Street, Suite 1200
Jacksonville, FL 32202
(904) 353-0890

Physically disabled; mental health; visually impaired; emotionally disturbed; youth; cultural organizations; Woman's Club of Jacksonville, Inc. (building funds for an accessible rest room for people who are disabled)

Only previous recipients of funding from this foundation are eligible to apply for another grant.

Typical grant range: $10,000 to $100,000

180
The Lucy Gooding Charitable Foundation Trust
10287 Shady Crest Lane
Jacksonville, FL 32221
(904) 737-8735

March of Dimes; Down Syndrome Association; Cerebral Palsy (rehabilitation program for kids); Girl Scouts (program for scouts who are disabled); Boy Scouts (program for scouts who are disabled); North Florida School of Special Education (speech therapy program)

Grants awarded to organizations located in the Jacksonville vicinity.

181
Janirve Foundation
255 South County Road
Palm Beach, FL 33480

Mentally and physically disabled; developmentally disabled; accessibility project; Goodwill Industries

Typical grant range: $10,000 to $50,000

182
John S. and James L. Knight Foundation
One Biscayne Tower, Suite 3800
Two S. Biscayne Blvd.
Miami, FL 33131
(305) 908-2600

Christmas in April (home repair program for people who are disabled); Breakthrough Club (services for youth who are mentally ill); Goodwill Industries of South Florida (training and employment program for people who are disabled)

Typical grant range: $15,000 to $200,000

183
The Lost Tree Village Charitable Foundation, Inc.
11555 Lost Tree Way
North Palm Beach, FL 33408
(561) 622-3780

Mental Health Association; Association for Retarded Citizens; Seagull Industries for the Disabled; Palm Beach Habilitation Center; Center for Independent Living (equipment); Children's Golf Foundation (special golf course for children who are disabled)

Grants awarded to organizations located in Palm Beach County and southern Martin County.

Typical grant range: $2,500 to $25,000

184
J.N. McArthur Foundation, Inc.
80 S.W. 8th Street, Suite 2110
Miami, FL 33130
(305) 374-8411

Miami Lighthouse for the Blind; United Cerebral Palsy; Miami Project to Cure Paralysis

Typical grant range: $500 to $15,000

185
The John E. & Aliese Price Foundation, Inc.
1279 Lavin Lane
North Fort Myers, FL 33917
(941) 656-0196

Physically disabled; visually impaired; Special Equestrians Horses and Handicapped

Most grants awarded to organizations located in the Fort Myers vicinity.

186
Publix Super Markets Charities
P.O. Box 407
Lakeland, FL 33802
(863) 688-1188

Physically disabled; visually impaired;
National Multiple Sclerosis Society

Grants awarded to organizations located
in Florida.

Typical grant range: $2,500 to $50,000

187
William G. Selby and Marie Selby Foundation
1800 Second Street, Suite 750
Sarasota, FL 34236
(941) 957-0442

Easter Seal Society; Goodwill Industries

Grants awarded to organizations located
in Sarasota and bordering counties.

Typical grant range: $5,000 to $50,000

188
The Southwest Florida Community Foundation, Inc.
12734 Kenwood Lane, Suite 72
Fort Myers, FL 33907
(941) 274-5900

Eden Florida (facility for therapy and
teaching for individuals who are autistic);
Down Syndrome Association (purchase a
van)

Grants awarded to organizations located
in Lee County and surrounding Counties.

189
The George B. Storer Foundation, Inc.
P.O. Box 1907
Islamorada, FL 33036
(305) 664-4822

Visually impaired; physically disabled;
Lighthouse for the Blind

Typical grant range: $5,000 to $100,000

190
The Wahlstrom Foundation, Inc.
3055 Cardinal Drive, Suite 106
P.O. Box 3276
Vero Beach, FL 32964
(561) 231-7513

Association for Retarded Citizens
(summer camp for children who are
developmentally delayed); National
Children's Reading Foundation (program
to help children with reading disabilities)

Grants awarded to organizations located
in Indian River County.

191
Wilson-Wood Foundation, Inc.
7188 Beneva Road
Sarasota, FL 34238
(941) 921-2856

Deaf Service Center; Mental Health
Community Centers; Mana-Sota
Lighthouse for the Blind (early
intervention program for children);
Southeastern Guide Dogs (van); Special
Skaters Society (ice rink time for kids
who are disabled); Sarasota Garden Club
(wheelchair access project); Easter Seal
Society (renovate classrooms); Girl
Scouts (program for girls who are
disabled)

Grants awarded to organizations located
in Sarasota and Manatee Counties.

Typical grant range: $4,000 to $20,000

192
Winn-Dixie Stores Foundation
5050 Edgewood Court
Jacksonville, FL 32254
(904) 783-5000

Visually impaired; physically disabled;
Lighthouse for the Blind

Grants awarded to organizations located
in areas of company operations (Winn-
Dixie).

Typical grant range: $2,500 to $30,000

GEORGIA

193
The Peyton Anderson Foundation, Inc.
577 Mulberry Street, Suite 1015
Macon, GA 31201
(912) 743-5359

Physically disabled; Central Georgia
Foundation for Speech and Hearing
(hearing aids)

Most grants awarded to organizations
located in Bibb County.

194
Callaway Foundation, Inc.
209 Broome Street
P.O. Box 790
LaGrange, GA 30241
(706) 884-7348

Recording for the Blind and Dyslexic;
Crawford Center for Therapeutic
Horsemanship; Deafness Research
Foundation; March of Dimes Birth
Defects; Canine Vision, Inc. (train guide
dogs)

Grants awarded to organizations located
in Georgia, with an emphasis in
LaGrange.

Typical grant range: $5,000 to $100,000

195
**The Community Foundation for
Greater Atlanta, Inc.**
The Hurt Building, Suite 449
Atlanta, GA 30303
(404) 688-5525

Mental Health Association of Metro
Atlanta; George West Mental Health
Foundation; Auditory Education Center

Grants awarded to organizations located
in the Atlanta vicinity.

Typical grant range: $1,000 to $15,000

196
Georgia Health Foundation
57 Executive Park South, N.E., Suite 315
Atlanta, GA 30329
(404) 636-2525

Jewish Family and Career Services
(wheelchair access to dental clinic);
Center for the Visually Impaired (services
for diabetics who are visually impaired);
Easter Seal Society, Inc. (program to help
people with head and spinal cord injury)

Grants awarded to organizations located
in Georgia.

197
Georgia Power Foundation, Inc.
Mail Bin 10230
241 Ralph McGill Blvd., N.E.
Atlanta, GA 30308
(404) 506-4669

Physically disabled; mental health; Brain
Injury Association

Grants awarded to organizations located
in Georgia.

198
Georgia-Pacific Foundation, Inc.
133 Peachtree Street, N.E.
Atlanta, GA 30303
(404) 652-4000

Physically disabled; Shepherd Spinal
Center; Special Education Center

Grants awarded to organizations located
in areas of company operations, with an
emphasis in Atlanta.

Typical grant range: $5,000 to $25,000

199
**John H. and Wilhelmina D. Harland
Charitable Foundation, Inc.**
Two Piedmont Center, Suite 106
Atlanta, GA 30305
(404) 264-9912

Physically disabled; developmentally
disabled; hearing impaired; speech
impaired; Canine Assistants; Friends of
Disabled Adults

Grants awarded to organizations located
in Georgia, with an emphasis in Atlanta.

200
The Imlay Foundation, Inc.
945 E. Paces Ferry Road, Suite 2450
Atlanta, GA 30326
(404) 239-1777

Special Olympics; Georgewest Mental
Health

Grants awarded to organizations located
in Atlanta.

Typical grant range: $1,000 to $15,000

201
**Mary Ryan & Henry G. Kuhrt
Foundation**
c/o SunTrust Bank, Atlanta
P.O. Box 4655 MC 221
Atlanta, GA 30302
(404) 588-7356

Goodwill Industries

Grants awarded to organizations located
in Georgia, with an emphasis in Atlanta.

202
Paul B. and Mildred Seydel Foundation
c/o John R. Seydel
1027 Peachtree Battle Avenue, N.W.
Atlanta, GA 30327
(404) 355-6537

Center for the Visually Handicapped;
American Foundation for the Blind

Most grants awarded to organizations
located in Georgia.

Typical grant range: $250 to $3,000

203
SunTrust Bank Atlanta Foundation
c/o SunTrust Bank, Atlanta
P.O. Box 4418, MC 041
Atlanta, GA 30302
(404) 588-8246

Speech impaired; physically disabled;
Atlanta Speech School

Most grants awarded to organizations
located in the Atlanta vicinity.

Typical grant range: $500 to $12,500

204
Waffle House Foundation, Inc.
P.O. Box 6450
Norcross, GA 30091

March of Dimes; Prevent Blindness

Most grants awarded to organizations
located in the Atlanta vicinity.

Typical grant range: $2,500 to $25,000

205
Joseph B. Whitehead Foundation
50 Hurt Plaza, Suite 1200
Atlanta, GA 30303
(404) 522-6755

Canine Assistants; Atlanta Speech School;
Easter Seals; Camp Twin Lakes (program
for children who are disabled); Chastain
Horse Park, Ltd. (building funds for a
therapeutic riding facility); Auditory
Education Center (program for children
who are hearing impaired); Cobb Street
Ministries (van for clients who are
disabled)

Grants awarded to organizations located
in the Atlanta vicinity.

Typical grant range: $50,000 to $400,000

206
**The Frances Wood Wilson
Foundation, Inc.**
250 E. Ponce De Leon Avenue, Suite 702
Decatur, GA 30030
(404) 370-0035

Mentally and physically disabled; speech
impaired

Most grants awarded to organizations
located in Georgia.

Typical grant range: $3,000 to $45,000

207
Robert W. Woodruff Foundation, Inc.
50 Hurt Plaza, Suite 1200
Atlanta, GA 30303
(404) 522-6755

George West Mental Health Foundation, Inc. (housing program for people who are mentally ill)

Grants awarded to organizations located in Atlanta.

Typical grant range: $250,000 to $1,000,000

HAWAII

208
Alexander & Baldwin Foundation
P.O. Box 3440
Honolulu, HI 96801
(808) 525-6642

Physically disabled; Goodwill Industries

209
Atherton Family Foundation
c/o Hawaii Community Foundation
900 Fort Street Mall, Suite 1300
Honolulu, HI 96813
(808) 537-6333

Mentally and physically disabled; hearing impaired; Hilo Association for Retarded Citizens; Special Olympics; Easter Seal Society; Hawaii Services on Deafness; The ARC of Maui, Inc.; Parent Participation Nursery School (building funds for ramps)

Grants awarded to organizations located in Hawaii.

Typical grant range: $5,000 to $50,000

210
James & Abigail Campbell Foundation
1001 Kamokila Blvd.
Kapolei, HI 96707
(808) 674-3122

Waianae Community Mental Health Center; Easter Seal Society; Hawaii Services on Deafness (sign language training program for families)

Grants awarded to organizations located in Hawaii.

Typical grant range: $1,000 to $25,000

211
Harold K.L. Castle Foundation
146 Hekili Street, Suite 203A
Kailua, HI 96734
(808) 262-9413

Physically disabled; independent living program; youth; Easter Seal Society; March of Dimes (prevent birth defects)

Grants awarded to organizations located in Hawaii.

Typical grant range: $10,000 to $150,000

212
Samuel N. and Mary Castle Foundation
733 Bishop Street, Suite 1275
Honolulu, HI 96813
(808) 522-1101

Learning Disabilities Association; Orton Dyslexia Society; Friends of the Children's Advocacy Center (training program for mental health professionals)

Grants awarded to organizations located in Hawaii.

Typical grant range: $2,000 to $30,000

213
Cooke Foundation, Limited
Hawaii Community Foundation
900 Fort Street Mall, Suite 1300
Honolulu, HI 96813
(808) 537-6333

Hawaii Services on Deafness; Mental Help Hawaii; Special Olympics; Very Special Arts Hawaii; Kona Historical Society (building funds for accessibility project); Hawaii Branch of Orton Dyslexia Society (program to assist teens with dyslexia or learning disabilities)

Grants awarded to organizations located in Hawaii.

Typical grant range: $2,500 to $25,000

214
Mary D. and Walter F. Frear Eleemosynary Trust
c/o Pacific Century Trust
P.O. Box 3170
Honolulu, HI 96802
(808) 538-4944

Mentally and physically disabled; hearing impaired; mental health; cultural programs; employment programs; Opportunities for the Retarded; Mental Help Hawaii; Hawaii Services on Deafness

Grants awarded to organizations located in Hawaii.

215
Hawaii Community Foundation
900 Fort Street Mall, Suite 1300
Honolulu, HI 96813
(808) 537-6333

Learning Disabilities Association; Mental Help Hawaii; Affordable Housing Alliance (coalition to house homeless people with mental illness); Kauai Economic Opportunity, Inc. (mental health program); Imua Rehab (speech therapy program for children); Parents and Children Together (speech therapy program)

Grants awarded to organizations located in Hawaii.

Typical grant range: $500 to $40,000

216
McInerny Foundation
c/o Pacific Century Trust
P.O. Box 3170
Honolulu, HI 96802
(808) 538-4944

Goodwill Industries; Mental Health Association; Alliance for the Mentally Ill; March of Dimes; Orton Dyslexia Society (workshops for teachers); Hale Kipa Properties (program for youth who are mentally disabled); Hawaii Centers for Independent Living (technology equipment for clients who are disabled); Winners at Work (job training for individuals who are disabled); Hawaii Services on Deafness (sign language interpreter)

Grants awarded to organizations located in Hawaii.

Typical grant range: $3,000 to $20,000

217
Sophie Russell Testamentary Trust
c/o Pacific Century Trust
P.O. Box 3170
Honolulu, HI 96802
(808) 538-4944

Mentally and physically disabled; youth; employment program; Opportunities for the Retarded; Goodwill Industries

Grants awarded to organizations located in Hawaii.

Typical grant range: $2,500 to $7,500

218
A. & E. Vidinha Charitable Trust
c/o Pacific Century Trust
P.O. Box 3170
Honolulu, HI 96802
(808) 538-4944

Easter Seal Society

Grants awarded to organizations located in Kauai.

219
Elsie H. Wilcox Foundation
c/o Pacific Century Trust
P.O. Box 3170
Honolulu, HI 96802
(808) 538-4944

Mental health; hearing impaired; physically disabled; Hawaii Services on Deafness (American Sign Language training program); Mental Health Association (public awareness program)

Typical grant range: $2,000 to $5,000

220
G.N. Wilcox Trust
c/o Pacific Century Trust
P.O. Box 3170
Honolulu, HI 96802
(808) 538-4944

Hawaii Special Olympics; Orton Dyslexia Society; Hawaii Centers for Independent Living; Hawaii Services on Deafness; Opportunities for the Retarded; Mental Health Association; Mental Help Hawaii; Community Work Day Program (assist clients who are disabled at home)

Grants awarded to organizations located in Hawaii.

Typical grant range: $1,000 to $15,000

IDAHO

221
The Leland D. Beckman Foundation
c/o Stephen E. Martin
P.O. Box 3189
Idaho Falls, ID 83403

Crossroad Counseling Services (mental health services); Development Workshop, Inc. (accessibility project for people in wheelchairs); Eastern Idaho Technical College (grant for a computer, scanner, and software to assist students with disabilities)

Grants awarded to organizations located in Idaho Falls.

Typical grant range: $1,000 to $7,000

222
Daugherty Foundation
c/o U.S. Bank
P.O. Box 51448
Idaho Falls, ID 83405
(208) 525-1667

Physically disabled; Shriners Hospital for Crippled Children

Typical grant range: $1,000 to $25,000

223

Harry W. Morrison Foundation, Inc.
3505 Crescent Rim Drive
Boise, ID 83706

Special Olympics

Grants awarded to organizations located in Boise.

Typical grant range: $500 to $10,000

ILLINOIS

224

Abbott Laboratories Fund
Dept. 379, Building 14C
100 Abbott Park Road
Abbott Park, IL 60064
(847) 937-6100

March of Dimes; Foundation for Special Education

Grants awarded to organizations located in areas of company operations (Abbott Laboratories).

Typical grant range: $2,000 to $50,000

225

G.J. Aigner Foundation, Inc.
5617 Dempster Street
Morton Grove, IL 60053
(847) 966-5782

Physically disabled; Easter Seal Society

Most grants awarded to organizations located in the Chicago vicinity.

Typical grant range: $1,000 to $10,000

226

AON Foundation
123 N. Wacker Drive
Chicago, IL 60606
(312) 701-3000

Mentally and physically disabled; visually impaired; Guiding Eyes for the Blind

Typical grant range: $5,000 to $100,000

227

Francis Beidler Charitable Trust
53 W. Jackson Blvd., Suite 530
Chicago, IL 60604
(312) 922-3792

Physically disabled; mental health

Grants awarded to organizations located in Illinois.

228

The Blowitz-Ridgeway Foundation
1 Northfield Plaza, Suite 230
Northfield, IL 60093
(847) 446-1010

Recording for the Blind and Dyslexic; Easter Seal Rehabilitation Center (building funds for an accessible home for adults who are developmentally disabled); Garfield Park Conservatory Alliance (horticulture therapy program for children who are disabled); Little Friends (group home for children with autism); Center for Enriched Living (parenting and health education program for mothers who are developmentally disabled); Chicago Lighthouse (assistive devices for students who are visually impaired); Deicke Center for Visual Rehabilitation (services for students who are visually impaired)

Grants awarded to organizations located in Illinois.

Typical grant range: $2,000 to $25,000

229
Helen Brach Foundation
55 W. Wacker Drive, Suite 701
Chicago, IL 60601
(312) 372-4417

Chicago Hearing Society; Chicago Lighthouse for the Blind; Rainbow Riders Horseback (program for people who are mentally and physically disabled); Institute for Therapy Through Arts (art therapy program for clients with various disabilities); Beacon Therapeutic School, Inc. (mental health services for homeless women and children); St. Mary of the Lake (program for children who are emotionally disturbed which allows them to stay in school); Lambs Foundation (job placement program for adults who are mentally disabled); Clearbrook Center (computer-based learning program for children who are developmentally disabled); Cove School, Inc. (tuition for a student who is learning disabled); St. Mary of Providence (elevator for people who are developmentally disabled)

Typical grant range: $3,000 to $30,000

230
The Chicago Community Trust
222 N. LaSalle Street, Suite 1400
Chicago, IL 60601
(312) 372-3356

Canine Companions for Independence; Housing Options for the Mentally Ill; Council for Disability Rights; Trilogy, Inc. (mental health services for the hispanic community); Chicago Women's Health Center (wheelchair accessibility project); Albany Park Community Center, Inc. (employment program for people who are recovering from being mentally ill)

Grants awarded to organizations located in Cook County, with an emphasis in Chicago.

Typical grant range: $5,000 to $100,000

231
Chicago Tribune Charities
435 N. Michigan Avenue
Chicago, IL 60611
(312) 222-4300

Goodwill Industries (job training program); Operation Able (employment or job training program for adults who are disabled)

Grants awarded to organizations located in the Chicago vicinity.

Typical grant range: $5,000 to $25,000

232
Chicago Tribune Foundation
435 N. Michigan Avenue
Chicago, IL 60611
(312) 222-4300

National Federation of the Blind (telephone newspaper project); Chicago Theater Foundation (auditions and workshops for actors who are disabled); Chicagoland Radio Information Service, Inc. (news and information services for listeners who are disabled)

Most grants awarded to organizations located in the Chicago vicinity.

Typical grant range: $3,000 to $30,000

233
Arie and Ida Crown Memorial
222 N. LaSalle Street, Suite 2000
Chicago, IL 60601
(312) 236-6300

Hearing impaired; physically disabled; Children's Hearing Institute

Most grants awarded to organizations located in the Chicago vicinity.

Typical grant range: $1,000 to $30,000

234
Doris and Victor Day Foundation, Inc.
1705 Second Avenue, Suite 424
Rock Island, IL 61201
(309) 788-2300

Mental health; Easter Seal Foundation (occupational therapy program); Independent Living Center (access ramps); Moore Memorial Library (accessibility project); Genesis Health Services Foundation (education and recreation programs for children with disabilities)

Grants awarded to organizations located in the Illinois/Iowa Quad Cities vicinity.

235
Evanston Community Foundation
828 Davis Street, Suite 300
Evanston, IL 60201
(847) 475-2402

Physically disabled; Lekotek (Computer Club for children with disabilities); Warren Cherry Preschool (education program for young children with special needs)

Grants awarded to organizations located in Evanston.

236
The Field Foundation of Illinois, Inc.
200 S. Wacker Drive, Suite 2080
Chicago, IL 60606
(312) 831-0910

Chicago Lighthouse for People Who Are Blind or Visually Impaired; Housing Opportunities and Maintenance for the Elderly (wheelchair lift); Visual Arts Project (program for individuals who are physically, mentally or emotionally disadvantaged)

Grants awarded to organizations located in the Chicago vicinity.

Typical grant range: $3,000 to $30,000

237
Julius Frankel Foundation
c/o Harris Trust & Savings Bank
111 W. Monroe Street
Chicago, IL 60603
(312) 461-2613

Visually impaired; hearing impaired; Recording for the Blind

Grants awarded to organizations located in Chicago.

Typical grant range: $10,000 to $50,000

238
Otto W. Lehmann Foundation
P.O. Box 11194
Chicago, IL 60611

Hadley School for the Blind; Illinois Foundation Dentistry for the Handicapped; Society for Prevention of Blindness; Peacock Camp for Crippled Children; Boy Scouts of America (program for children with special needs); House of the Good Shepherd (adults with special needs)

Grants awarded to organizations located in the Chicago vicinity.

239
John D. and Catherine T. MacArthur Foundation
140 S. Dearborn Street
Chicago, IL 60603
(312) 726-8000

Mental Health Policy and Research; SSI Coalition for a Responsible Safety Net (grant to assist job training programs for people who are disabled)

Typical grant range: $50,000 to $500,000

240
Mazza Foundation
225 W. Washington Street, Suite 1300
Chicago, IL 60606
(312) 444-9300

Physically disabled; visually impaired

Most grants awarded to organizations located in Chicago.

Typical grant range: $5,000 to $50,000

241
Robert R. McCormick Tribune Foundation
435 N. Michigan Avenue, Suite 770
Chicago, IL 60611
(312) 222-3512

Lansing Association for Retarded Children; Chicago Lighthouse for the Blind; Good Shepherd Center for Exceptional Children; Clearbrook Center for the Handicapped; Garden Center for the Handicapped; Association for Retarded Citizens; Blue Island Citizens for Persons with Developmental Disabilities, Inc.; Chicago Association for Retarded Citizens; Chicago Fund on Aging and Disability; Glenkirk Foundation for the Retarded; Illinois Easter Seal Society, Inc.; Illinois Special Olympics; Proviso Township Mental Health Center; Ray Graham Association for People with Disabilities

Most grants awarded to organizations located in the Chicago vicinity.

Typical grant range: $20,000 to $100,000

242
The Nalco Foundation
One Nalco Center
Naperville, IL 60563
(630) 305-1556

Special Olympics; Chicago Lighthouse for the Blind; Recording for the Blind & Dyslexic, Inc.; Boy Scouts of America (special needs program); Good Shepherd Center for Exceptional Children (program for children who are developmentally disabled); Lester & Rosalie Anixter Center (Chicago Hearing Society Youth Program); United Cerebral Palsy Association (assistive technology); Legal Clinic for the Disabled, Inc. (advocacy for children with special needs); St. Mary of Providence School (building funds for accessibility program); Dyslexia Association (multi-media equipment for a classroom); Easter Seal Society (computer training and job placement); Association for Citizens with Handicaps (early childhood intervention program)

Grants awarded to organizations located in areas of company operations (Nalco Chemical Co.).

Typical grant range: $1,000 to $25,000

243
The Northern Trust Company Charitable Trust
c/o The Northern Trust Company
Community Affairs Division
50 South LaSalle Street
Chicago, IL 60675
(312) 444-4059

Recording for the Blind & Dyslexic; Housing Options for the Mentally Ill; Association for People with Disabilities (therapeutic riding program); Jewish Children's Bureau (program for families with a child who is disabled)

Most grants awarded to organizations located in the Chicago vicinity.

Typical grant range: $1,500 to $20,000

244

Frank E. Payne and Seba B. Payne Foundation
c/o Bank of America
Personal Trust Department
231 S. LaSalle Street, 2nd Floor
Chicago, IL 60697
(312) 828-1785

Learning disabled; Recording for the Blind and Dyslexic; Easter Seal Society

245

Peoria Area Community Foundation
124 S.W. Adams Street, Suite M1
Peoria, IL 61602
(309) 674-8730

Physically disabled; Easter Seals (pony walker for rehabilitation)

Grants awarded to organizations located in the Peoria vicinity.

Typical grant range: $1,000 to $10,000

246

Polk Bros. Foundation, Inc.
420 N. Wabash Avenue, Suite 204
Chicago, IL 60611
(312) 527-4684

Chicago Hearing Society (hearing and vision screenings); Access Living of Metropolitan Chicago (teach independence skills to people who are disabled); Chicago Association for Retarded Citizens (early intervention program for children); Chicagoland Radio Information Service (project for youth with disabilities)

Grants awarded to organizations located in the Chicago vicinity.

Typical grant range: $5,000 to $100,000

247

The Quaker Oats Foundation
Quaker Tower
321 N. Clark Street
Chicago, IL 60610
(312) 222-7377

Emotionally disturbed; physically disabled; National Lekotek Center (project for children who are developmentally impaired)

Grants awarded to organizations located in areas of company operations (Quaker Oats Co.), with an emphasis in Illinois.

Typical grant range: $1,500 to $25,000

248

The Retirement Research Foundation
8765 W. Higgins Road, Suite 401
Chicago, IL 60631
(312) 714-8080

Deicke Center for Visual Rehabilitation; Jewish Association for Residential Care (services and residential facilities for adults who are developmentally disabled); Avenues to Independence (program for adults who are developmentally disabled); Sertoma Centre, Inc. (van for adults who are developmentally disabled); Fillmore Center for Human Services (mental health program); Northwestern University (national study of late-onset psychiatric disorders)

Most grants awarded to organizations helping the elderly.

Typical grant range: $3,000 to $100,000

249

Dr. Scholl Foundation
11 S. LaSalle Street, Suite 2100
Chicago, IL 60603
(312) 782-5210

Mentally and physically disabled; visually impaired; youth

Typical grant range: $5,000 to $50,000

250
State Farm Companies Foundation
One State Farm Plaza
Bloomington, IL 61710
(309) 766-2161

Goodwill Industries; Eye Bank
Association of America; Dole Foundation
for Employment of People with
Disabilities

Grants awarded to organizations located
in areas of company operations (State
Farm Insurance Companies).

Typical grant range: $1,000 to $25,000

251
United Airlines Foundation
P.O. Box 66100
Chicago, IL 60666

Special Olympics; Guide Dogs of
America; Muscular Dystrophy
Association; March of Dimes Birth
Defects Foundation

Grants awarded to organizations located
in areas of company operations.

Typical grant range: $5,000 to $100,000

252
**Washington Square Health
Foundation, Inc.**
875 N. Michigan Avenue, Suite 3516
Chicago, IL 60611
(312) 664-6488

Physically disabled; health care; Easter
Seal Society

Grants awarded to organizations located
in the Chicago vicinity.

253
W.P. and H.B. White Foundation
540 Frontage Road, Suite 3240
Northfield, IL 60093
(847) 446-1441

Mentally and physically disabled;
dyslexia

Grants awarded to organizations located
in the Chicago vicinity.

Typical grant range: $5,000 to $20,000

254
Woods Fund of Chicago
70 W. Madison Street, Suite 2010
Chicago, IL 60602
(312) 782-2698

Access Living of Metropolitan Chicago
(research on people who are disabled);
SSI Coalition for a Responsible Safety
Net (employment program for people
who are disabled)

Most grants awarded to organizations
located in the Chicago vicinity.

Typical grant range: $5,000 to $40,000

INDIANA

255
John W. Anderson Foundation
402 Wall Street
Valparaiso, IN 46383
(219) 462-4611

Physically and mentally disabled;
Northwest Indiana Special Education
Cooperative

Most grants awarded to organizations
located in Northwest Indiana.

Typical grant range: $5,000 to $50,000

256
The Arvin Foundation, Inc.
One Noblitt Plaza
Box 3000
Columbus, IN 47202
(812) 379-3207

Indiana Special Olympics; ARC; Easter
Seals; Association of the Deaf; American
Association of Deaf and Blind; Disabled
American Veterans; Fayette Co. March of
Dimes; Multiple Sclerosis Association of
America

Grants awarded to organizations located
in areas of company operations (Arvin
Industries, Inc.).

Typical grant range: $1,000 to $15,000

257
Ayres Foundation, Inc.
6355 Morenci Trail
Indianapolis, IN 46268
(317) 299-2200

Special Olympics of Indiana

Grants awarded to organizations located in Indiana, with an emphasis in Indianapolis.

Typical grant range: $1,000 to $10,000

258
Ball Brothers Foundation
222 S. Mulberry Street
P.O. Box 1408
Muncie, IN 47308
(765) 741-5500

Indiana Special Olympics; East Central Indiana Therapeutic Riding

Grants awarded to organizations located in Indiana.

Typical grant range: $1,500 to $60,000

259
George and Frances Ball Foundation
P.O. Box 1408
Muncie, IN 47308
(765) 741-5500

Physically disabled; East Central Indiana Therapeutic Riding

Most grants awarded to organizations located in Muncie.

Typical grant range: $10,000 to $75,000

260
The Clowes Fund, Inc.
320 N. Meridian Street, Suite 316
Indianapolis, IN 46204-1722
(317) 833-0144

Visually impaired; Recording for the Blind & Dyslexic

Typical grant range: $5,000 to $50,000

261
Olive B. Cole Foundation, Inc.
6207 Constitution Drive
Fort Wayne, IN 46804
(219) 436-2182

DeKalb County ARC; Indiana Lakeland Girl Scout Council (accessibility project for scouts who are disabled)

Most grants awarded to organizations located in Noble County.

Typical grant range: $3,000 to $20,000

262
Dearborn County Community Foundation
P.O. Box 292
239 Walnut Street, Suite 200
Lawrenceburg, IN 47205
(812) 537-5617

North Dearborn American Legion (accessibility program for the community center); Aurora To Lawrenceburg Trail (accessible trail for people who are disabled)

Grants awarded to organizations located in Dearborn County.

263
The Dekko Foundation, Inc.
1208 E. Lakeside Drive
P.O. Box 548
Kendallville, IN 46755
(219) 347-1278

Physically and mentally disabled; Special Education Cooperative; Anthony Wayne Rehabilitation Center for Handicapped and Blind, Inc.; Crossroad Mental Health Center

Typical grant range: $1,000 to $50,000

264
**Elkhart County Community
Foundation, Inc.**
P.O. Box 279
Elkhart, IN 46515
(219) 295-8761

Physically disabled; Mental Health
Association; Oaklawn Foundation for
Mental Health (playground equipment for
children)

Grants awarded to organizations located
in Elkhart County.

Typical grant range: $500 to $10,000

265
Foellinger Foundation, Inc.
520 E. Berry Street
Fort Wayne, IN 46802
(219) 422-2900

Physically disabled; visually impaired;
youth

Grants awarded to organizations located
in Allen County.

Typical grant range: $5,000 to $150,000

266
**Eugene and Marilyn Glick Foundation
Corporation**
P.O. Box 40177
Indianapolis, IN 46240
(317) 469-5858

Physically disabled; Therapeutic Riding
Center for Handicapped People

Grants awarded to organizations located
in Indianapolis.

Typical grant range: $250 to $8,000

267
**Greater Johnson County Community
Foundation**
18 W. Jefferson
P.O. Box 217
Franklin, IN 46131
(317) 738-2213

Physically disabled; Meals on Wheels
(meals delivered to people who are
disabled); Brent Williams Memorial Fund
(health and education program for people
who are learning disabled)

Most grants awarded to organizations
located in Johnson County.

268
**The Health Foundation of Greater
Indianapolis**
Marott Center, 1st Floor
342 Massachusetts Avenue
Indianapolis, IN 46204
(317) 630-1805

Midtown Community Mental Health
Center; Muscular Dystrophy Association

Grants awarded to organizations located
in Marion County and seven contiguous
counties in central Indiana.

Typical grant range: $1,000 to $30,000

269
The Indianapolis Foundation
615 N. Alabama Street, Room 119
Indianapolis, IN 46204
(317) 634-7497

Midtown Community Mental Health
Center (social and recreation program for
patients with a mental illness); WFYI
TelePlex (Indiana Radio Reading's dial-up
reading service for people who are blind);
Indianapolis-Marion County Public
Library (program to make print materials
accessible to people who are blind,
visually impaired or learning-disabled)

Grants awarded to organizations located
in Marion County.

Typical grant range: $3,000 to $60,000

270
Irwin-Sweeney-Miller Foundation
P.O. Box 808
Columbus, IN 47202
(812) 372-0251

Physically disabled; Easter Seal
Committee (Resource and Awareness
Coalition for Persons with Disabilities
conference)

Grants awarded to organizations located
in the Columbus vicinity.

Typical grant range: $2,500 to $20,000

271
Lilly Endowment Inc.
2801 N. Meridian Street
Indianapolis, IN 46208
(317) 924-5471

Special Olympics; Muscular Dystrophy
Association; Indiana Deaf Camps
Foundation

Grants awarded to organizations located in
Indiana, with an emphasis in Indianapolis.

Typical grant range: $2,500 to $100,000

272
The Lincoln National Foundation, Inc.
915 S. Clinton Street
P.O. Box 7822
Fort Wayne, IN 46802
(219) 455-3868

Mentally and physically disabled; Very
Special Arts

Typical grant range: $5,000 to $50,000

273
Magee-O'Connor Foundation, Inc.
P.O. Box 800
800 Standard Federal Plaza
Fort Wayne, IN 46801-0800
(219) 422-0800

Physically disabled; visually impaired

Grants awarded to organizations located
in Fort Wayne.

Typical grant range: $2,500 to $15,000

274
**The Walter E. Wallace & Rose M.
Wallace Crippled Children's Fund**
Firstar Trust Services
Trust Department
P.O. Box 818
Richmond, IN 47375
(765) 965-2301

Physically and mentally disabled; youth

Grants awarded to organizations located
in Wayne County.

Typical grant range: $3,000 to $10,000

IOWA

275
Roy J. Carver Charitable Trust
202 Iowa Avenue
Muscatine, IA 52761
(319) 263-4010

Visually impaired; physically disabled;
Iowa Braille & Sight Saving School

Grants awarded to organizations located
in Iowa.

Typical grant range: $25,000 to $200,000

276
**The Ralph & Sylvia G. Green
Charitable Foundation**
c/o Green Associates, Inc.
1801 2nd Avenue
Des Moines, IA 50314

Very Special Arts

Grants awarded to organizations located
in Des Moines.

Typical grant range: $500 to $10,000

277
The Hall-Perrine Foundation, Inc.
115 Third Street, S.E., Suite 803
Cedar Rapids, IA 52401
(319) 362-9079

Physically disabled; Goodwill Industries

Grants awarded to organizations located
in Linn County.

Typical grant range: $5,000 to $120,000

278
Charles Hockenberry Foundation
c/o City National Bank
P.O. Box 279
Shenandoah, IA 51601
(712) 246-2205

Mentally and physically disabled; youth

Grants awarded to organizations located
in Page County.

279
The Fred Maytag Family Foundation
P.O. Box 366
Newton, IA 50208
(515) 791-0395

Physically and mentally disabled; visually
impaired

Most grants awarded to organizations
located in Newton and Des Moines.

Typical grant range: $2,000 to $30,000

280
R.J. McElroy Trust
KWWL Building, Suite 318
500 E. Fourth Street
Waterloo, IA 50703
(319) 291-1299

Mentally and physically disabled;
Muscular Dystrophy Association; Alliance
for the Mentally Ill (therapy program for
children); Miracle in the Motion, Inc.
(therapeutic horseback riding program for
people who are physically or mentally
disabled)

Typical grant range: $3,000 to $50,000

281
Mid-Iowa Health Foundation
550 39th Street, Suite 104
Des Moines, IA 50312
(515) 277-6411

Physically disabled; visually impaired;
Iowa Radio Reading Information Service
(reading service for the people who are
blind); Toward the Home Accessibility
Program (education program teaching
youth to assist the elderly and people who
are disabled)

Grants awarded to organizations located
in the Polk County vicinity.

Typical grant range: $1,000 to $25,000

282
Pella Rolscreen Foundation
c/o Pella Corporation
102 Main Street
Pella, IA 50219
(515) 628-1000

Physically disabled; Tracy Christian
Reformed Church (accessibility project
for people who are disabled)

Grants awarded to organizations located
in areas of company operations (Pella
Corp.).

283
**The Principal Financial Group
Foundation, Inc.**
711 High Street
Des Moines, IA 50392
(515) 247-5091

Physically disabled; visually impaired;
cultural programs; National Multiple
Sclerosis Society; Goodwill Industries

Grants awarded to organizations located
in Iowa, with an emphasis in Des Moines.

Typical grant range: $3,000 to $60,000

284
Pauline Stolteben Foundation Trust
c/o American Trust & Savings Bank
895 Town Clock Plaza
Dubuque, IA 52001
(319) 589-0817

Catholic Guild for the Blind

Typical grant range: $500 to $5,000

KANSAS

285
Dane G. Hansen Foundation
P.O. Box 187
Logan, KS 67646
(785) 689-4832

Physically disabled; visually impaired;
Kansas Elks Training Center for the
Handicapped

Typical grant range: $5,000 to $25,000

286
Hutchinson Community Foundation
P.O. Box 298
Hutchinson, KS 67504
(316) 663-5293

Physically disabled; mental health; Youth
Transitional Services (program to help
students who are physically disabled); Not
the Usual Mental Health Program
(program to increase the awareness of
mental illness)

Grants awarded to organizations located
in Reno County.

287
Kansas Health Foundation
309 East Douglas
Wichita, KS 67202
(316) 262-7676

Mental Health Consortium; Harvey
County Special Education

Grants awarded to organizations located
in Kansas.

Typical grant range: $25,000 to $150,000

KENTUCKY

288
James Graham Brown Foundation, Inc.
4350 Brownsboro Road, Suite 200
Louisville, KY 40207-1681
(502) 896-2440

Kentucky Special Olympics; Kentucky
Easter Seal Society, Inc.; March of Dimes
Birth Defects Foundation; Visually
Impaired Preschool Services; Recording
for the Blind, Inc.; American Printing
House for the Blind, Inc.

Grants awarded to organizations located
in Kentucky, with an emphasis in
Louisville.

Typical grant range: $10,000 to $250,000

289
**The Community Foundation of
Louisville, Inc.**
Waterfront Plaza
325 W. Main Street, Suite 1110
Louisville, KY 40202
(502) 585-4649

Council for Retarded Citizens; The de Paul
School (private school dedicated to
teaching children with dyslexia)

Grants awarded to organizations located
in Louisville.

Typical grant range: $1,000 to $15,000

290
**Foundation for the Tri-State
Community, Inc.**
P.O. Box 2096
1401 Winchester Avenue
Ashland, KY 41105
(606) 324-3888

Huntington City Mission (accessibility
project); Forrest Management Corporation
(mental health services); City of Kenova
(funds for a ramp); Interfaith Volunteer
Caregivers Network (program for people
who are disabled); Kentucky Highlands
Museum Society, Inc. (rest room
accessibility project)

291

The Gheens Foundation, Inc.
One Riverfront Plaza, Suite 705
Louisville, KY 40202
(502) 584-4650

Hearing impaired; mentally and physically disabled

Most grants awarded to organizations located in Kentucky, with an emphasis in Louisville.

Typical grant range: $5,000 to $60,000

292

The Humana Foundation, Inc.
The Humana Building
500 W. Main Street
P.O. Box 1438
Louisville, KY 40201
(502) 580-3041

Mentally and physically disabled; Special Olympics; March of Dimes

Typical grant range: $5,000 to $100,000

293

The MacLean Foundation, Inc.
P.O. Box 6249
Louisville, KY 40206

Recording for the Blind and Dyslexic; Guide Dog Foundation for the Blind; American Printing House for the Blind; Dogs for the Deaf

Most grants awarded to organizations located in Louisville.

Typical grant range: $250 to $3,000

294

Margaret Hall Foundation, Inc.
291 S. Ashland Avenue
Lexington, KY 40502
(606) 269-2236

Shedd Academy (school for students who are learning disabled); Aseltine School (school for students who are emotionally disturbed or learning disabled)

Typical grant range: $3,000 to $13,000

295

Fred B. and Opal S. Woosley Foundation, Inc.
900 Kentucky Home Life Building
Louisville, KY 40202

Mentally and physically disabled; visually impaired; youth; education

Grants awarded to organizations located in the Jefferson County vicinity.

296

Lester E. Yeager Charitable Trust B
P.O. Box 964
Owensboro, KY 42302

Special Olympics; American Printing House for the Blind; Autism Society of America

Typical grant range: $1,000 to $10,000

LOUISIANA

297

Charles T. Beaird Foundation
330 Marshall Street, Suite 1112
Shreveport, LA 71101-3015
(318) 221-8276

Visually impaired; mentally disabled; Louisiana Association for the Blind

Grants awarded to organizations located in the Shreveport vicinity.

298

The Community Foundation of Shreveport-Bossier
401 Edwards Street, Suite 1111
Shreveport, LA 71101
(318) 221-0582

Physically and mentally disabled; Association for Retarded Citizens

Grants awarded to organizations located in Caddo and Bossier Parishes.

Typical grant range: $5,000 to $25,000

299
German Protestant Orphan Asylum Association
P.O. Box 158
Mandeville, LA 70470
(504) 674-5328

Mentally disabled; learning disabled; youth; Center for Development and Learning (teacher training program relating to students who are learning disabled)

Grants awarded to organizations located in Louisiana.

Typical grant range: $2,000 to $20,000

300
The Lupin Foundation
3715 Prytania Street, Suite 304
New Orleans, LA 70115
(504) 897-6125

Physically disabled; March of Dimes (research)

Grants awarded to organizations located in Louisiana.

301
The Magale Foundation, Inc.
c/o Bank One, Louisiana, N.A.
P.O. Box 21116
Shreveport, LA 71154
(318) 226-2382

Special Olympics

Typical grant range: $2,000 to $10,000

MAINE

302
Libra Foundation
Box 17516
Portland, ME 04112
(207) 879-6280

Aroostook Mental Health Center; The Chocolate Church Arts Center (accessible rest room project); Counseling Services, Inc. (camp program for children who are disabled)

Grants awarded to organizations located in Maine.

303
Edward E. and Hilda C. Rosen Foundation
Bangor Savings Bank, Trust Dept.
P.O. Box 930
Bangor, ME 04402
(207) 942-5211

Physically disabled; visually impaired; Society for Handicapped Children and Adults

Typical grant range: $500 to $7,000

304
Simmons Foundation, Inc.
c/o Perkins, Thompson, Hinckley & Keddy
One Canal Plaza
P.O. Box 426
Portland, ME 04112
(207) 774-2635

United Cerebral Palsy

Grants awarded to organizations located in Maine.

Typical grant range: $1,000 to $8,000

305
UNUM Foundation
2211 Congress Street, Mail Stop P349
Portland, ME 04122
(207) 770-4378

Northeast Hearing and Speech Center; Guiding Eyes for the Blind, Inc.; Tri-County Mental Health Services; National Multiple Sclerosis Society; Very Special Arts; Pine Tree Society for Handicapped Children & Adults; Spurwink School (therapeutic riding program)

Grants awarded to organizations located in Maine.

Typical grant range: $2,500 to $25,000

MARYLAND

306
Charles S. Abell Foundation, Inc.
8401 Connecticut Avenue, Suite 1111
Chevy Chase, MD 20815
(301) 652-2224

Very Special Arts; Community of Hope
(support a Psychiatric Social Worker);
Bread For The City (food for people who
are disabled); St. John's Community
Services (employment opportunities for
young people who are mentally disabled);
Anchor Mental Health Association, Inc.
(housing for homeless people who are
mentally ill); Special Olympics (sports
program for people who are
developmentally disabled)

Typical grant range: $5,000 to $40,000

307
The Abell Foundation, Inc.
111 S. Calvert Street, Suite 2300
Baltimore, MD 21202
(410) 547-1300

Visually impaired; physically disabled;
youth

Grants awarded to organizations located
in Maryland, with an emphasis in
Baltimore.

Typical grant range: $3,000 to $65,000

308
The Baltimore Community Foundation
The Latrobe Building
Two E. Read Street, 9th Floor
Baltimore, MD 21202
(410) 332-4171

Lions Camp for the Deaf; The League:
Serving People with Physical Disabilities;
Baltimore Crisis Response, Inc.
(homebound program for people who are
mentally ill); The Children's Fresh Air
Society Fund (camp program for children
who are disabled); Joseph C. Briscoe
Career Center/Students Helping Other
People (high school program for students
who are emotionally disturbed or
physically disabled)

Grants awarded to organizations located
in the Baltimore vicinity.

309
Thomas W. Bradley Foundation, Inc.
c/o Pierson, Pierson & Nolan
217 E. Redwood Street, Suite 2020
Baltimore, MD 21202
(410) 727-4136

Children who are mentally or physically
disabled; The Handicap Athletic Program

Most grants awarded to organizations
located in Maryland.

310
Eugene B. Casey Foundation
800 S. Frederick Avenue, Suite 100
Gaithersburg, MD 20877
(301) 948-4595

Visually impaired; physically disabled;
Recording for the Blind and Dyslexic

Typical grant range: $10,000 to $100,000

311

Clark-Winchcole Foundation
#3 Bethesda Metro Center, Suite 550
Bethesda, MD 20814
(301) 654-3607

Mentally disabled; hearing impaired;
mental health; Alexander Graham Bell
Association for the Deaf

Most grants awarded to organizations
located in the Washington, DC vicinity.

Typical grant range: $5,000 to $30,000

312

**Crown Central Petroleum
Foundation, Inc.**
One North Charles Street
Baltimore, MD 21201
(410) 539-7400

Goodwill Industries

Grants awarded to organizations located
in Maryland.

Typical grant range: $150 to $1,000

313

**Morris Goldseker Foundation of
Maryland, Inc.**
The Latrobe Building
Two E. Read Street, 9th Floor
Baltimore, MD 21202
(410) 837-5100

Physically disabled; mental health;
Goodwill Industries

Grants awarded to organizations located
in the Baltimore vicinity.

Typical grant range: $5,000 to $100,000

314

The Emmert Hobbs Foundation, Inc.
c/o Friedman & Friedman
409 Washington Ave., Suite 900
Towson, MD 21204
(410) 494-0100

Developmentally disabled; accessibility
projects; Mental Health Association
(annual campaign); League with People
with Disabilities (fitness center);
Springrove Hospital Center (services for
people who are disabled); Springfield
State Hospital (services for people who
are disabled)

Grants awarded to organizations located
in the Baltimore vicinity.

Typical grant range: $2,000 to $10,000

315

Hoffberger Foundation, Inc.
The Exchange, Suite 215
1122 Kenilworth Drive
Towson, MD 21204
(410) 321-8750

Physically disabled; visually impaired;
Baltimore League for Handicapped

Grants awarded to organizations located
in the Baltimore vicinity.

316

**Ensign C. Markland Kelly, Jr.
Memorial Foundation, Inc.**
1406 Fidelity Building
Baltimore, MD 21201
(410) 837-8822

Physically disabled; Cystic Fibrosis
Foundation

Grants awarded to organizations located
in the Baltimore vicinity.

Typical grant range: $1,000 to $15,000

317

The Marion I. and Henry J. Knott Foundation, Inc.
3904 Hickory Avenue
Baltimore, MD 21211
(410) 235-7068

Mentally and physically disabled; Bright Vision Therapeutic Riding; Baltimore Association for Retarded Citizens

Typical grant range: $5,000 to $50,000

318

George Preston Marshall Foundation
35 Wisconsin Circle, Suite 525
Chevy Chase, MD 20815
(301) 654-7774

Physically and mentally disabled; employment programs; Columbia Lighthouse for the Blind; Easter Seal Society (camper program for children); Bethesda Academy of Performing Arts (program for children who are hearing impaired)

Typical grant range: $1,000 to $10,000

319

The W. O'Neil Foundation
5454 Wisconsin Avenue, Suite 730
Chevy Chase, MD 20815

Visually impaired; mental health; Society for the Blind

Typical grant range: $5,000 to $25,000

MASSACHUSETTS

320

John W. Alden Trust
State Street Bank & Trust Co.
225 Franklin Street
Boston, MA 02110
(617) 664-3358

Physically disabled; visually impaired; youth; National Braille Press

Most grants awarded to organizations located in Massachusetts.

Typical grant range: $3,000 to $15,000

321

The Paul and Edith Babson Foundation
c/o Nichols & Pratt
50 Congress Street
Boston, MA 02109
(617) 523-6800

Wellesley Congregational Church (home for adults who are mentally disabled); Talking Information Center (radio broadcasting program for people who are blind or dyslexic)

322

Adelaide Breed Bayrd Foundation
28 Pilgrim Road
Melrose, MA 02176

Visually impaired; hearing impaired; Easter Seal Society

Grants awarded to organizations located in the Malden vicinity.

323

The Boston Foundation, Inc.
One Boston Place, 24th Floor
Boston, MA 02108
(617) 723-7415

Very Special Arts; Disability Law Center, Inc.; Carroll Center for the Blind, Inc.; Shriver Center (expand Massachusetts Network of Information Providers for People with Disabilities); Bunker Hill Community College Foundation (adaptive technology program for students who are disabled)

Grants awarded to organizations located in the Boston vicinity.

Typical grant range: $20,000 to $55,000

324
The Boston Globe Foundation II, Inc.
P.O. Box 2378
135 Morrissey Blvd.
Boston, MA 02107
(617) 929-2895

Very Special Arts; Museum of Fine Arts (accessibility project); Talking Information Center (on-air reading program for listeners who are blind or dyslexic); D.E.A.F., Inc. (independent living program for older teens)

Grants awarded to organizations located in the Boston vicinity.

Typical grant range: $2,000 to $20,000

325
Cabot Family Charitable Trust
c/o Cabot-Wellington LLC
70 Federal Street
Boston, MA 02110-1906
(617) 451-1744

National Braille Press (books for children who are blind); Boston Women's Fund (program for women with disabilities); WGBH (technology project for people who are visually or hearing impaired); Outdoor Explorations (program to support greater acceptance of community housing for people with disabilities)

326
Roberta M. Childs Charitable Foundation
P.O. Box 639
North Andover, MA 01845

Physically disabled

Grants awarded to organizations located in Massachusetts.

Typical grant range: $1,000 to $3,500

327
Clipper Ship Foundation, Inc.
c/o Grants Management Associates
77 Summer Street, 8th Floor
Boston, MA 02110
(617) 426-7172

Mental Health Association; The Learning Disabilities Network; Very Special Arts Massachusetts (early learning center and a special needs program); Partners for Youth with Disabilities (independence program); South Shore ARC (elevator); Vision Foundation (project for the elderly who are visually impaired); Boston Guild for the Hard of Hearing (hearing tests for migrant children); Citizens' Housing and Planning Association (home ownership project for people who are disabled); Pass It On, Inc. (provides used medical equipment for people who are disabled)

Grants awarded to organizations located in the Boston vicinity.

Typical grant range: $5,000 to $25,000

328
Community Foundation of Western Massachusetts
1500 Main Street, Suite 1800
P.O. Box 15769
Springfield, MA 01115
(413) 732-2858

Massachusetts State Association of the Deaf; The ARC of Franklin County; Alliance for the Mentally Ill; Gandara Mental Health Center, Inc.; Community Music School of Springfield, Inc. (wheelchair lift); Ronald McDonald House (accessible playground); YMCA (accessible lift for pool); New England Business Associates (employment program for people who are disabled)

Grants awarded to organizations located in western Massachusetts.

329
Irene E. and George A. Davis Foundation
301 Chestnut Street
East Longmeadow, MA 01028
(413) 734-8336

Physically disabled; mental health; Goodwill Industries

Typical grant range: $2,500 to $25,000

330
Eastman Charitable Foundation
31 Milk Street, Room 501
Boston, MA 02109
(617) 423-5599

Morgan Memorial Goodwill, Inc. (job training program for people who are disabled); National Braille Press (services and publications for people who are visually impaired)

Most grants awarded to organizations located in Massachusetts.

Typical grant range: $250 to $2,500

331
Fidelity Foundation
82 Devonshire Street
Boston, MA 02109
(617) 563-6806

Physically disabled; visually impaired; Shriner's Hospital for Crippled Children

Grants awarded to organizations located in areas of company operations, with an emphasis in Massachusetts.

Typical grant range: $3,000 to $40,000

332
Harcourt General Charitable Foundation, Inc.
27 Boylston Street
Chestnut Hill, MA 02467
(617) 232-8200

Visually impaired; Research to Prevent Blindness

Grants awarded to organizations located in the Boston vicinity.

Typical grant range: $1,000 to $50,000

333
Amelia Peabody Charitable Fund
10 Post Office Square N., Suite 995
Boston, MA 02109
(617) 451-6178

Physically disabled; visually impaired; accessibility projects; National Braille Press

Most grants awarded to organizations located in Massachusetts.

Typical grant range: $7,500 to $100,000

334
Amelia Peabody Foundation
One Hollis Street
Wellesley, MA 02181
(781) 237-6468

National Braille Press; Recording for the Blind

Grants awarded to organizations located in Massachusetts.

Typical grant range: $5,000 to $75,000

335
The Peabody Foundation, Inc.
c/o Sherburne, Powers, and Needham, P.C.
One Beacon Street
Boston, MA 02108

Physically disabled; rehabilitation; research

Grants awarded to organizations located in Massachusetts, with an emphasis in Boston.

336
Ellis L. Phillips Foundation
233 Commonwealth Avenue, Apt. 2
Boston, MA 02116
(617) 424-7607

Physically disabled; emotionally disturbed; cultural programs; youth; accessibility project

Typical grant range: $5,000 to $15,000

337
A.C. Ratshesky Foundation
77 Summer Street
Boston, MA 02110
(617) 426-7172

Physically disabled; cultural programs

Most grants awarded to organizations located in the Boston vicinity.

338
The Mabel Louise Riley Foundation
c/o Warner & Stackpole L.L.P.
75 State Street
Boston, MA 02109
(617) 951-9100

Mental Health and Retardation Center; Chinese Culture Institute (accessibility project for people who are physically disabled); Germaine Lawrence, Inc. (residential treatment program for girls who are emotionally disturbed)

Most grants awarded to organizations located in the Boston vicinity.

Typical grant range: $5,000 to $50,000

339
Rowland Foundation, Inc.
P.O. Box 13
Cambridge, MA 02238

Visually impaired; education; National Society to Prevent Blindness

Typical grant range: $10,000 to $75,000

340
Sawyer Charitable Foundation
200 Newbury Street, 4th Floor
Boston, MA 02116
(617) 262-2414

Visually impaired; Carroll Center for the Blind

Typical grant range: $5,000 to $30,000

341
State Street Foundation
225 Franklin Street, 12th Floor
Boston, MA 02215
(617) 664-3381

Boston University Center for Psychiatric Rehabilitation; The Carroll Center for the Blind; March of Dimes; Recording for the Blind & Dyslexic; Partners for Youth with Disabilities

Grants awarded to organizations located in the Boston vicinity.

Typical grant range: $5,000 to $50,000

MICHIGAN

342
Ann Arbor Area Community Foundation
201 S. Main, Suite 801
Ann Arbor, MI 48104-2113
(734) 663-0401

Early Learning Center (summer program for preschool children with autism); Therapeutic Riding, Inc. (therapeutic riding program for youth)

Grants awarded to organizations located in the Ann Arbor vicinity.

343
Bay Area Community Foundation
703 Washington Avenue
Bay City, MI 48708
(517) 893-4438

Dyslexia; physically disabled; Scottish Rite Bodies (program for people with dyslexia)

Grants awarded to organizations located in Bay County.

Typical grant range: $500 to $10,000

344
Besser Foundation
123 N. Second Avenue, Suite 4
Alpena, MI 49707
(517) 354-4722

Northeast Michigan Depressive/Manic
Depressive Association; Christian Record
Braille Foundation (camp for children
who are blind)

Most grants awarded to organizations
located in Alpena.

Typical grant range: $2,000 to $50,000

345
The Carls Foundation
333 W. Fort Street, Suite 1940
Detroit, MI 48226
(313) 965-0990

War Memorial Hospital (Speech and
Hearing Clinic); Lutheran Child and
Family Service (recreation equipment
used in therapy for youth who are
emotionally or learning impaired);
Tuscola Intermediate School District
(grant to test children who are hearing or
learning impaired); Traverse Bay Area
Intermediate School District (sound
amplification equipment for classrooms
and library to assist children who are
hearing and learning impaired); The
University of Michigan, Center for the
Child and Family (library materials and
furniture to be used by clients who are
deaf); Detroit Institute for Children
(medical care and therapy for people
who are developmentally disabled)

Grants awarded to organizations located
in Michigan.

Typical grant range: $3,000 to $20,000

346
Colina Foundation
1 Heritage Place, Suite 220
Southgate, MI 48195
(734) 283-8847

Dyslexia Institute (teacher training
program)

Typical grant range: $500 to $8,000

347
**Community Foundation for
Southeastern Michigan**
333 W. Fort Street, Suite 2010
Detroit, MI 48226
(313) 961-6675

Deaf, Hearing and Speech Center; Very
Special Arts Michigan; Shriners Hospital
for Crippled Children; Penrickton Center
for Blind Children; Recording for the
Blind and Dyslexic; Boys and Girls Club
(program for youth who are physically
disabled); Sertoma Foundation (scholarship
program for students who are hearing
impaired)

Grants awarded to organizations located
in southeastern Michigan.

Typical grant range: $2,000 to $30,000

348
**The Community Foundation of the
Holland/Zeeland Area**
70 West 8th Street, Suite 100
Holland, MI 49423-3166
(616) 396-6590

Lakeshore Center for Independent Living;
Holland Area Arts Council (accessibility
project)

Grants awarded to organizations located
in the Holland/Zeeland vicinity.

Typical grant range: $1,000 to $20,000

349
Detroit Armory Corporation
1943 Common Road
Warren, MI 48092

Visually impaired; Leader Dogs for the
Blind

Grants awarded to organizations located
in Michigan, with an emphasis in Detroit.

Typical grant range: $1,000 to $5,000

350
Detroit Edison Foundation
2000 Second Avenue, Room 1046 WCB
Detroit, MI 48226
(313) 235-9271

Physically disabled; visually impaired;
Goodwill Industries

Typical grant range: $2,000 to $30,000

351
Frey Foundation
48 Fountain Street, N.W., Suite 200
Grand Rapids, MI 49503
(616) 451-0303

Physically disabled; dyslexia; youth;
education

Typical grant range: $5,000 to $75,000

352
The Gerber Foundation
4747 West 48th Street, Suite 153
Fremont, MI 49412-8119
(231) 924-3175

Visually impaired; hearing impaired

Grants awarded to organizations located
in areas of company operations (Gerber
Products Co.).

Typical grant range: $3,500 to $25,000

353
The Rollin M. Gerstacker Foundation
P.O. Box 1945
Midland, MI 48641
(517) 631-6097

Emotionally disturbed; Michigan Eye
Bank and Transplant Center; Mental
Health Association; Association for
Children's Mental Health; National
Multiple Sclerosis Society; National
Alliance for Research on Schizophrenia
and Depression

Typical grant range: $5,000 to $50,000

354
Irving S. Gilmore Foundation
136 E. Michigan Avenue, Suite 615
Kalamazoo, MI 49007
(616) 342-6411

Visually impaired; Goodwill Industries;
Leader Dogs for the Blind

Grants awarded to organizations located
in the Kalamazoo vicinity.

Typical grant range: $10,000 to $100,000

355
**Grand Haven Area Community
Foundation, Inc.**
One South Harbor
Grand Haven, MI 49417
(616) 842-6378

Physically disabled; Kandu Industries (job
training and support services for people
who are disabled)

Grants awarded to organizations located
in northwest Ottawa County, with an
emphasis in Grand Haven.

356
The Grand Rapids Foundation
209-C Waters Building
161 Ottawa Avenue, N.W.
Grand Rapids, MI 49503
(616) 454-1751

Physically disabled; United Cerebral
Palsy Association

Grants awarded to organizations located
in the Grand Rapids vicinity.

Typical grant range: $5,000 to $60,000

357
Herrick Foundation
840 W. Long Lake Road, Suite 200
Troy, MI 48098-6358
(248) 258-3021

Mentally and physically disabled; learning
disabled; Association for Retarded Citizens;
Lenawee Riding for the Handicapped

Typical grant range: $5,000 to $100,000

358
The Jackson Community Foundation
230 W. Michigan Avenue
Jackson, MI 49201
(517) 787-1321

Physically disabled; Society for
Handicapped Children and Adults
(adaptive computer equipment)

Grants awarded to organizations located
in Jackson County.

Typical grant range: $1,000 to $30,000

359
Kalamazoo Foundation
151 S. Rose Street, Suite 332
Kalamazoo, MI 49007
(616) 381-4416

Kalamazoo Northside Non-profit Housing
Corp. (housing for people who are
physically disabled); Kalamazoo
Homestead, Inc. (housing for residents
with mental illness); MRC Industries, Inc.
(community center for individuals with
mental illness)

Grants awarded to organizations located
in Kalamazoo County.

Typical grant range: $10,000 to $100,000

360
W.K. Kellogg Foundation
One Michigan Avenue East
Battle Creek, MI 49017
(616) 968-1611

Physically and mentally disabled; Partners
for Disabled Youth

Typical grant range: $5,000 to $100,000

361
**Knight Family Charitable and
Educational Foundation**
215 N. Talbot Street
Addison, MI 49220
(517) 547-6131

United Cerebral Palsy

Most grants awarded to organizations
located in Michigan.

Typical grant range: $500 to $5,000

362
The Kresge Foundation
3215 W. Big Beaver Road
Troy, MI 48007
(248) 643-9630

Greenwich Association for Retarded
Citizens; League for the Hearing
Impaired; Main Line Art Center
(accessibility project); Blind Association
(renovation grant); St. Joseph Institute for
the Deaf (school for children who are
deaf); The Hill Center (building funds for
a school for children with learning
disabilities)

Emphasis on building grants.

Typical grant range: $100,000 to $750,000

363
McGregor Fund
333 W. Fort Street, Suite 2090
Detroit, MI 48226
(313) 963-3495

Wayne State University (Infant Mental
Health Program); Children's Home of
Detroit (psychiatric care for children who
are emotionally and mentally impaired);
Methodist Children's Home Society (grant
to help children who are emotionally
impaired)

Grants awarded to organizations located
in Detroit.

Typical grant range: $20,000 to $60,000

364
May Mitchell Royal Foundation
c/o Comerica Bank-Midland
P.O. Box 993
201 McDonald Street
Midland, MI 48640
(517) 839-2270

Visually impaired; physically disabled;
Leader Dogs for the Blind

Typical grant range: $1,000 to $20,000

365

The Skillman Foundation
600 Renaissance Center, Suite 1700
Detroit, MI 48243
(313) 568-6360

Mental health; developmentally disabled;
youth

Typical grant range: $25,000 to $200,000

366

Steelcase Foundation
P.O. Box 1967
Grand Rapids, MI 49501
(616) 246-4695

Physically disabled; learning disabled;
mental health; Grand Rapids Community
College Foundation (accessibility project);
Pilgrimage Family Therapy Center
(counseling and education program for
people who are learning disabled)

Grants awarded to organizations located
in areas of company operations (Steelcase,
Inc.).

Typical grant range: $5,000 to $50,000

367

The Whiting Foundation
901 Citizens Bank Building
328 S. Saginaw Street
Flint, MI 48502
(810) 767-3600

Physically disabled; visually impaired;
youth

Grants awarded to organizations located
in the Flint vicinity.

Typical grant range: $1,000 to $25,000

368

Matilda R. Wilson Fund
100 Renaissance Center, 34th Floor
Detroit, MI 48243
(313) 259-7777

Visually impaired; mental health;
Readings for the Blind; Southwest Detroit
Community Mental Health Services

Typical grant range: $10,000 to $60,000

MINNESOTA

369

Andersen Foundation
c/o Andersen Corporation
100 Fourth Avenue North
Bayport, MN 55003
(651) 439-5150

Hearing impaired; visually impaired;
Deafness Research Foundation

Typical grant range: $7,500 to $200,000

370

Hugh J. Andersen Foundation
P.O. Box 204
Bayport, MN 55003
(651) 439-1557

Learning Disabilities Association;
Alliance for the Mentally Ill

Typical grant range: $2,000 to $30,000

371

Bayport Foundation, Inc.
P.O. Box 204
Bayport, MN 55003
(651) 439-1557

Visually impaired; hearing impaired;
Goodwill Industries

Most grants awarded to organizations
located in Minnesota.

372

F.R. Bigelow Foundation
600 Norwest Center
55 E. Fifth Street
St. Paul, MN 55101
(651) 224-5463

Alliance for the Mentally Ill; Lao Family
Community (mental health program for
Hmong youth and families); Lifeworks
Services, Inc. (communication equipment
for people who are developmentally
disabled); Mounds View Public Schools
(mental health program for children);
Central Presbyterian Church (accessibility
project)

Grants awarded to organizations located
in the St. Paul vicinity.

Typical grant range: $10,000 to $75,000

373
The Blandin Foundation
100 Pokegama Avenue North
Grand Rapids, MN 55744
(218) 326-0523

Physically disabled; developmentally
disabled; Forget-Me-Not Foundation
(therapeutic horseback riding program)

Grants awarded to organizations located
in Minnesota.

374
Otto Bremer Foundation
445 Minnesota Street, Suite 2000
St. Paul, MN 55101
(651) 227-8036

United Cerebral Palsy; March of Dimes;
Deafness Education and Advocacy
Foundation; Northern Pines Mental
Health Center, Inc.; Deaf Blind Services;
School for the Blind; Learning Disabilities
of Minnesota; Marshall County Group
Homes, Inc. (wheelchair accessible van);
Friendship, Inc. (employment program for
people who are developmentally disabled);
Metropolitan Center for Independent
Living, Inc. (accessibility project); Devils
Lake Mayor's Committee for Employment
of People with Disabilities; The ARC
(cultural program); Central Minnesota
Elder Network (mental health program)

Grants awarded to organizations located
in areas of company operations (Bremer
Bank).

Typical grant range: $2,000 to $30,000

375
The Bush Foundation
E-900 First National Bank Bldg.
332 Minnesota Street
St. Paul, MN 55101
(651) 227-0891

Deaf Blind Services Minnesota, Inc.;
Exchange Club Center for Family Unity
(program for people who are hearing
impaired); Camp Grandir, Inc. (program
for children and families struggling with
mental illness)

Typical grant range: $25,000 to $100,000

376
The Cargill Foundation
P.O. Box 5690
Minneapolis, MN 55440
(612) 742-6290

Learning disabled; visually impaired;
Special Olympics

Grants awarded to organizations located
in the Minneapolis-St. Paul vicinity.

Typical grant range: $5,000 to $40,000

377
Albert W. Cherne Foundation
P.O. Box 975
Minneapolis, MN 55440
(612) 944-4378

Learning Disabilities Association; Girl
Scout Council (program for girls who are
physically disabled); Junior Achievement
(special needs program); Children's
Healthcare (Speech-Language Pathology
Department)

Grants awarded to organizations located
in the Minneapolis-St. Paul vicinity.

Typical grant range: $3,500 to $15,000

378
Deluxe Corporation Foundation
P.O. Box 64235
St. Paul, MN 55164
(651) 483-7842

Physically disabled; mental health;
Special Olympics; Cerebral Palsy
Association

Grants awarded to organizations located
in areas of company operations (Deluxe
Corp.).

Typical grant range: $2,500 to $25,000

379
**The Jaye F. and Betty F. Dyer
Foundation**
4670 Norwest Center
90 South 7th Street
Minneapolis, MN 55402
(612) 337-8194

Physically disabled; Holy Rosary Church
(accessibility project)

380
Ecolab Foundation
Ecolab Center
St. Paul, MN 55102
(651) 293-2259

Minnesota Foundation for Better Hearing
& Health (program for children who are
hearing impaired); Pacer Center (provide
information, training and education to the
parents of children who are physically
disabled); Lifeworks Services
(employment program and living skills
training for people who are physically
disabled)

381
Edwards Memorial Trust
c/o Private Financial Services
332 Minnesota Street
St. Paul, MN 55101
(651) 244-0924

Mental health; physically disabled

Grants awarded to organizations located
in the St. Paul vicinity.

382
General Mills Foundation
P.O. Box 1113
Minneapolis, MN 55440
(612) 540-7891

Special Olympics; ARC; Mental Health
Association; March of Dimes Birth
Defects Foundation; Hearing and Speech
Center; Very Special Arts Iowa;
Clovernook Home and School for the
Blind; Cystic Fibrosis Foundation;
Learning Disabilities Association, Inc.

Grants awarded to organizations located
in areas of company operations (General
Mills, Inc.).

Typical grant range: $2,000 to $75,000

383
Graco Foundation
P.O. Box 1441
Minneapolis, MN 55440
(612) 623-6684

Special Olympics

Grants awarded to organizations located
in areas of company operations (Graco
Inc.), with an emphasis in Minneapolis.

Typical grant range: $3,000 to $50,000

384
Honeywell Foundation
Honeywell Plaza
P.O. Box 524
Minneapolis, MN 55440
(612) 951-0431

March of Dimes; Foundation for Blind
Children; Gompers Center for the
Handicapped

Grants awarded to organizations located
in areas of company operations
(Honeywell, Inc.), with an emphasis in
Minneapolis.

Typical grant range: $2,000 to $25,000

385
**International Multifoods Charitable
Foundation**
P.O. Box 2942
Minneapolis, MN 55402
(612) 340-3300

Mental Health Association; Sports for the
Physically Challenged

Grants awarded to organizations located
in areas of company operations
(International Multifoods Corp.).

Typical grant range: $1,000 to $6,000

386
Kopp Family Foundation
7701 France Avenue South, Suite 500
Edina, MN 55435
(612) 920-3322

Hearing and Service Dogs of Minnesota;
Volunteer Braille Services; St. Andrew's
Crippled Children's Clinic

Grants awarded to organizations located
in Minnesota.

387
Mardag Foundation
600 Norwest Center
55 5th Street East
St. Paul, MN 55101
(651) 224-5463

Visually impaired; Independent School District (program for children who have a behavioral or mental health problem)

Grants awarded to organizations located in Minnesota.

Typical grant range: $5,000 to $50,000

388
The McKnight Foundation
Suite 600 TCF Tower
121 S. Eighth Street
Minneapolis, MN 55402
(612) 333-4220

Learning Disabilities Association; Very Special Arts; Legal Aid Society of Minneapolis (program for children who are emotionally or behaviorally disabled)

Typical grant range: $20,000 to $250,000

389
The Medtronic Foundation
7000 Central Avenue, N.E.
Minneapolis, MN 55432
(612) 514-3024

United Cambodian Assoc. of Minnesota (mental health education program)

Grants awarded to organizations located in areas of company operations (Medtronic, Inc.).

Typical grant range: $2,000 to $25,000

390
Ordean Foundation
501 Ordean Building
424 W. Superior Street
Duluth, MN 55802
(218) 726-4785

Physically disabled; mental health; speech impaired; youth; United Cerebral Palsy; Mental Health Association of Minnesota

Grants awarded to organizations located in the Duluth vicinity.

Typical grant range: $5,000 to $75,000

391
The Jay and Rose Phillips Family Foundation
Ten Second Street, N.E., Suite 200
Minneapolis, MN 55413
(612) 623-1654

Foundation for the Junior Blind; Canine Companions for Independence; Vision Loss Resources, Inc.; The Disability Institute; Center for the Partially Sighted; National Multiple Sclerosis Society; Mental Health Association; Jewish Family and Children's Services (program for people who are physically disabled)

Grants awarded to organizations located in Minnesota.

Typical grant range: $1,000 to $25,000

392
Red Wing Shoe Company Foundation
314 Main Street
Red Wing, MN 55066
(612) 388-8211

Special Olympics of Minnesota

Grants awarded to organizations located in the Red Wing vicinity.

393
ReliaStar Foundation
20 Washington Ave. South, Route 0941
Minneapolis, MN 55401
(612) 342-7443

Mentally and physically disabled; emotionally disturbed; rehabilitation

Most grants awarded to organizations located in Minneapolis.

394
The Saint Paul Foundation, Inc.
600 Norwest Center
St. Paul, MN 55101
(651) 224-5463

Minnesota Foundation for Better Hearing & Speech; Recording for the Blind & Dyslexic, Inc.; Shriner's Hospital for Crippled Children; Hamm Memorial Psychiatric Clinic; Independent School District, Mounds View Public Schools (project for children with behavior or mental health problems)

Most grants awarded to organizations located in the St. Paul vicinity.

Typical grant range: $1,000 to $35,000

395
Star Tribune Foundation
425 Portland Avenue
Minneapolis, MN 55488
(612) 673-7051

Learning disabled; physically disabled; Special Olympics; Learning Disabilities Association

Grants awarded to organizations located in the Minneapolis vicinity.

Typical grant range: $2,000 to $25,000

396
TCF Foundation
444 Cedar Street, Suite 220
St. Paul, MN 55101
(651) 291-4097

March of Dimes; Goodwill Industries; Opportunity Partners, Inc. (employment program for people who are physically disabled)

Grants awarded to organizations located in Minnesota.

MISSISSIPPI

397
William Robert Baird Charitable Trust
c/o Citizens National Bank
512 22nd Avenue
P.O. Box 911
Meridian, MS 39302
(601) 693-1331

Mississippi Special Olympics

Typical grant range: $2,500 to $10,000

MISSOURI

398
Anheuser-Busch Foundation
1 Busch Place
St. Louis, MO 63118
(314) 577-2453

Hearing impaired; mentally and physically disabled; Central Institute for the Deaf

Grants awarded to organizations located in areas of company operations (Anheuser-Busch Companies).

Typical grant range: $5,000 to $75,000

399
The H & R Block Foundation
4435 Main Street, Suite 500
Kansas City, MO 64111
(816) 932-8324

Swope Parkway Health Center (mental health program); Ozanam (program for youth who are learning disabled or emotionally disturbed); The Camping Connection (camp for children who are physically disabled)

400
Allen P. and Josephine B. Green Foundation
P.O. Box 523
Mexico, MO 65265
(573) 581-5568

Physically disabled; developmentally disabled; hearing impaired; visually impaired; youth; Share and Care Center for Special Needs (equipment and toys for adults and children who are developmentally disabled)

Grants awarded to organizations located in the Mexico, Missouri vicinity.

Typical grant range: $1,000 to $15,000

401
Hall Family Foundation
P.O. Box 419580, Mail Drop 323
Kansas City, MO 64141
(816) 274-8516

Mentally and physically disabled; mental health; Special Olympics

Grants awarded to organizations located in Kansas City.

Typical grant range: $15,000 to $250,000

402
Hallmark Corporate Foundation
P.O. Box 419580, Mail Drop 323
Kansas City, MO 64141
(816) 545-6906

Physically disabled; mental health; Foundation for Crippled Children

Grants awarded to organizations located in areas of company operations (Hallmark Cards, Inc.), with an emphasis in Kansas City.

Typical grant range: $2,000 to $25,000

403
William T. Kemper Foundation
P.O. Box 13095
Kansas City, MO 64199
(816) 234-2985

Physically and mentally disabled; Cerebral Palsy Research Foundation

Most grants awarded to organizations located in Missouri.

Typical grant range: $10,000 to $70,000

404
St. Louis Community Foundation
319 N. 4th Street, Suite 501
St. Louis, MO 63102
(314) 588-8200

Learning Disabilities Association; Delta Gamma Center for Children with Visual Impairment; White Oak Academy (school for students who are learning disabled)

Grants awarded to organizations located in the St. Louis vicinity.

405
Webb Foundation
7711 Carondelet Avenue, Suite 410
St. Louis, MO 63105
(314) 862-6220

Physically disabled; youth

Typical grant range: $2,000 to $30,000

406
Whitaker Foundation
1034 S. Brentwood Blvd., Suite 402
St. Louis, MO 63117
(314) 726-5734

Hearing impaired; physically disabled; cultural programs; House Ear Institute

Grants awarded to organizations located in St. Louis.

MONTANA

407

Dufresne Foundation
P.O. Box 1929
Great Falls, MT 59403
(406) 452-9414

Montana Special Olympics; School for the Deaf and Blind

Most grants awarded to organizations located in Montana.

408

The Montana Power Foundation, Inc.
40 E. Broadway
Butte, MT 59701
(406) 497-2602

Montana Special Olympics; Ronald McDonald House (accessibility project); Toys for Tots (gift program for teenagers who are disabled); Boys and Girls Ranch (program for youth who are emotionally disturbed); Dillon Library (add a ramp to satisfy the requirements of the Americans With Disabilities Act)

Grants awarded to organizations located in areas of company operations.

409

Sample Foundation, Inc.
14 N. 24th Street
P.O. Box 279
Billings, MT 59103
(406) 245-6342

Physically disabled; developmentally disabled; accessibility projects; recreation; Midland Empire Riding Academy for the Handicapped

Most grants awarded to organizations located in Montana.

Typical grant range: $1,000 to $10,000

410

The Tomorrow and You Foundation
2620 Fourth Avenue
Great Falls, MT 59405
(406) 454-1433

Mental health; physically disabled

Few grants awarded.

Most grants awarded to organizations located in Great Falls.

NEBRASKA

411

Oliver & Ferrol Barklage Foundation Trust
c/o Norwest Bank Nebraska, N.A.
10010 Regency Center, Suite 300
Omaha, NE 68114
(402) 536-2470

Eastern Nebraska Wheelchair Athletic Association; Radio Talking Book Services (closed-circuit receivers); School for the Deaf (sports complex); Ollie Webb Center (program for children who are visually impaired)

Most grants awarded to organizations located in Omaha.

Typical grant range: $2,000 to $10,000

412

Fremont Area Community Foundation
92 W. Fifth Street
P.O. Box 182
Fremont, NE 68025
(402) 721-4252

Radio Talking Books (equipment)

Grants awarded to organizations located in the Fremont vicinity.

Typical grant range: $500 to $7,500

413
Bernard K. & Norma F. Heuermann Foundation
c/o Northwest Bank NE, N.A.
Trust Department
1919 Douglas Street
Omaha, NE 68102

Mentally and physically disabled; youth; Association for Retarded Citizens

Grants awarded to organizations located in Nebraska.

Typical grant range: $1,500 to $20,000

414
Lincoln Community Foundation, Inc.
215 Centennial Mall South, Suite 200
Lincoln, NE 68508
(402) 474-2345

Physically disabled; Rape/Spouse Abuse Crisis Center (accessibility project for people who are physically disabled)

Grants awarded to organizations located in the Lincoln vicinity.

415
Mid-Nebraska Community Foundation, Inc.
315 N. Dewey, Suite 219
P.O. Box 1321
North Platte, NE 69103
(308) 534-3315

Physically disabled; North Platte Children's Museum (accessibility project)

Typical grant range: $1,000 to $5,000

416
Omaha Community Foundation
1623 Farnam Street, Suite 600
Omaha, NE 68102
(402) 342-3458

Lake Bristol Square Neighborhood Council (lawn care program for people who are disabled and the elderly); Child Saving Institute (foster care for children who are emotionally disabled); Visiting Nurses Association (respite care for children who have multiple disabilities)

Grants awarded to organizations located in the Omaha vicinity.

417
Edgar and Frances Reynolds Foundation, Inc.
P.O. Box 1492
Grand Island, NE 68801
(308) 384-0957

WRBH Radio for the Blind

Grants awarded to organizations located in Nebraska, with an emphasis on Grand Island.

Typical grant range: $2,000 to $30,000

418
Robert D. Wilson Foundation
8805 Indian Hills Drive, Suite 280
Omaha, NE 68114
(402) 390-0390

Radio-Talking Books; Omaha Hearing School for Children

Most grants awarded to organizations located in Nebraska.

Typical grant range: $3,000 to $10,000

419
Woods Charitable Fund, Inc.
P.O. Box 81309
Lincoln, NE 68501
(402) 474-0707

Lincoln Lancaster County Child Guidance Center (mental health services); People First of Nebraska, Inc. (services for people who are developmentally disabled); Union College (assistive technology program for people who are learning disabled)

Most grants awarded to organizations located in Lincoln.

Typical grant range: $2,000 to $25,000

NEVADA

420
The E.L. Cord Foundation
One East 1st Street, Suite 901
Reno, NV 89501
(702) 323-0373

Mentally and physically disabled;
Association for Retarded Citizens

Most grants awarded to organizations
located in northern Nevada.

Typical grant range: $5,000 to $75,000

421
Lied Foundation Trust
3907 W. Charleston Blvd.
Las Vegas, NV 89102
(702) 878-1559

Mentally disabled; hearing impaired

Typical grant range: $25,000 to $750,000

422
Nell J. Redfield Foundation
P.O. Box 61
1755 E. Plumb Lane, Suite 212
Reno, NV 89504
(702) 323-1373

Physically disabled; youth

Most grants awarded to organizations
located in Reno.

Typical grant range: $2,000 to $100,000

423
E.L. Wiegand Foundation
Wiegand Center
165 W. Liberty Street
Reno, NV 89501
(775) 333-0310

Physically disabled; hearing impaired;
Special Olympics

Typical grant range: $5,000 to $75,000

NEW HAMPSHIRE

424
The Barker Foundation
P. O. Box 328
Nashua, NH 03061

Visually impaired; physically disabled;
Easter Seal Society

Most grants awarded to organizations
located in New Hampshire.

Typical grant range: $500 to $10,000

425
Foundation for Seacoast Health
100 Campus Drive, Suite 1
Portsmouth, NH 03801-5892
(603) 422-8200

Seacoast Mental Health Center; Seacoast
HealthNet (mental health awareness
program); AIDS Response of the Seacoast
(mental health services); York County
Community Action Corporation (hearing
aids)

Typical grant range: $2,000 to $50,000

426
Agnes M. Lindsay Trust
660 Chestnut Street
Manchester, NH 03104
(603) 669-1366

Physically disabled; accessibility project

Typical grant range: $1,000 to $20,000

NEW JERSEY

427
John Bickford Foundation
P.O. Box 1945
Morristown, NJ 07962

Mental Health Association; Depressive
and Manic Depressive Association

Typical grant range: $1,000 to $10,000

428
Fund for the New Jersey Blind, Inc.
153 Halsey Street
P.O. Box 47017
Newark, NJ 07101
(973) 648-2324

Union County Association for the Blind; National Federation of the Blind; Lions Eye Bank; New Jersey Blind Citizens; New Jersey Recreation for the Blind; Blind Women's Society; New Jersey Camp for Blind Children

Grants awarded to organizations located in New Jersey.

Typical grant range: $750 to $5,000

429
The Healthcare Foundation of New Jersey
75 Livingston Avenue
Roseland, NJ 07068
(973) 535-8200

Mentally disabled; developmentally disabled; Association for Retarded Citizens

Typical grant range: $5,000 to $100,000

430
The Hyde and Watson Foundation
437 Southern Blvd.
Chatham Township, NJ 07928
(973) 966-6024

Physically disabled; emotionally disturbed; Rolling Hills Girl Scout Council (accessibility project); Herbert G. Birch Early Childhood Center (program for children with disabilities); Institute for Nursing (building funds for accessibility project); Jewish Board of Family and Children's Services (expand mental health center); St. Clares Riverside Foundation (program for people who are mentally disabled); College of Saint Elizabeth (vehicle for people who are disabled)

Typical grant range: $5,000 to $25,000

431
The Robert Wood Johnson Foundation
P.O. Box 2316
Princeton, NJ 08543
(609) 452-8701

Mental Health Association; March of Dimes Birth Defects Foundation; Easter Seal Society; Association for Retarded Citizens; National Institute on Deafness and Other Communication Disorders; Mays Mission for the Handicapped, Inc.

432
F.M. Kirby Foundation, Inc.
17 DeHart Street
P.O. Box 151
Morristown, NJ 07963
(973) 538-4800

Physically disabled; visually impaired; United Cerebral Palsy

Most grants awarded to organizations located in Morristown, New Jersey and the Raleigh-Durham vicinity, North Carolina.

Typical grant range: $10,000 to $30,000

433
Blanche and Irving Laurie Foundation, Inc.
P.O. Box 53
Roseland, NJ 07068

Visually impaired; speech impaired; physically disabled; Helen Keller International

Most grants awarded to organizations located in New Jersey.

Typical grant range: $2,500 to $50,000

434
The Curtis W. McGraw Foundation
c/o Drinker, Biddle & Reath
P.O. Box 627
Princeton, NJ 08542
(609) 497-7011

Physically disabled; visually impaired; mental health; Recording for the Blind and Dyslexic; Sagebrush Equine Training Center for the Handicapped

Typical grant range: $1,000 to $25,000

435
The MCJ Foundation
310 South Street
Morristown, NJ 07960
(973) 540-1946

Physically and mentally disabled;
Goodwill Industries

Grants awarded to organizations located
in Newark.

Typical grant range: $1,000 to $40,000

436
Fannie E. Rippel Foundation
180 Mount Airy Road, Suite 200
Basking Ridge, NJ 07920
(908) 766-0404

Physically disabled; Matheny School and
Hospital (technology program that uses a
person's bioelectric signals for wheelchair
movement)

Typical grant range: $50,000 to $150,000

437
L.P. Schenck Fund
c/o PNC Private Bank
41 Oak Street
Ridgewood, NJ 07450
(201) 652-8499

Mental health; visually impaired;
Community Center for Mental Health

Grants awarded to organizations located
in New Jersey.

Typical grant range: $2,000 to $35,000

438
**The Schumann Fund for
New Jersey, Inc.**
21 Van Vleck Street
Montclair, NJ 07042
(973) 509-9883

The Chen School (education and services
for children who are developmentally
disabled)

Grants awarded to organizations located
in New Jersey.

Typical grant range: $5,000 to $50,000

439
The Arnold A. Schwartz Foundation
c/o Bivona, Kunzman, Cohen, et al.
15 Mountain Blvd.
Warren, NJ 07059
(908) 757-7800

Physically disabled; youth; education;
Cerebral Palsy Association

Typical grant range: $1,000 to $8,000

440
Turrell Fund
21 Van Vleck Street
Montclair, NJ 07042
(973) 783-9358

Mentally and physically disabled; hearing
impaired; mental health; youth; education;
Association for Retarded Citizens

Typical grant range: $5,000 to $45,000

441
Victoria Foundation, Inc.
40 S. Fullerton Avenue
Montclair, NJ 07042
(973) 783-4450

Our Lady of Good Counsel Elementary
School (learning disabilities specialist);
Independence: A Family of Services, Inc.
(program that helps youth who are
emotionally disturbed); Newark
Renaissance House, Inc. (grant for the
Training Institute in Infant Mental Health)

Typical grant range: $20,000 to $100,000

442
**The Warner-Lambert Charitable
Foundation**
201 Tabor Road
Morris Plains, NJ 07950
(973) 540-2243

Mentally and physically disabled; Special
Olympics; National Organization on
Disability

Grants awarded to organizations located
in areas of company operations (Warner-
Lambert Co.).

Typical grant range: $5,000 to $50,000

NEW MEXICO

443

Albuquerque Community Foundation
P.O. Box 36960
Albuquerque, NM 87176
(505) 883-6240

Very Special Arts; hearing impaired; developmentally disabled; Independent Living Resource Center (American Sign Language Classes); RCI, Inc. (develop adaptive equipment for people with severe disabilities); Albuquerque Little Theater (deaf interpreter); Barrett Foundation (program to help women with chronic mental illness)

Grants awarded to organizations located in the Albuquerque vicinity.

Typical grant range: $1,000 to $5,000

444

The R.D. and Joan Dale Hubbard Foundation
P.O. Box 2498
Ruidoso, NM 88355
(505) 258-5919

New Mexico Special Olympics

445

J.F Maddox Foundation
P.O. Box 2588
Hobbs, NM 88241
(505) 393-6338

Mentally and physically disabled; Association for Retarded Citizens

Typical grant range: $3,000 to $75,000

446

McCune Charitable Foundation
345 E. Alameda Street
Santa Fe, NM 87501
(505) 983-8300

Mental health; physically disabled; hearing impaired; youth

Grants awarded to organizations located in New Mexico.

Typical grant range: $3,500 to $40,000

447

Santa Fe Community Foundation
P.O. Box 1827
Santa Fe, NM 87504
(505) 988-9715

Challenge New Mexico Therapeutic Riding (program for people who are mentally or physically disabled); School for the Deaf (Natural Helpers Program); The Salvation Army (job training program for people who are mentally disabled)

Most grants awarded to organizations located in the Santa Fe vicinity.

NEW YORK

448

The Achelis Foundation
767 Third Avenue, 4th Floor
New York, NY 10017
(212) 644-0322

Eye Bank for Sight Restoration; Cooke Foundation for Special Education (independent living program for young people with disabilities); Theatre Development Fund (sign language at plays); Resources for Children with Special Needs (program for parents with children who are physically disabled)

Grants awarded to organizations located in New York City.

Typical grant range: $5,000 to $50,000

449
Altman Foundation
220 E. 42nd Street, Suite 411
New York, NY 10017
(212) 682-0970

The Coalition of Voluntary Mental Health Agencies, Inc.; The Mental Health Association; Visiting Nurse Service of New York (mental health program); New York Service Program for Older People, Inc. (provide mental health services at organizations that assist the elderly); Young Adult Institute, Inc. (program for people who are mentally disabled or developmentally disabled)

Grants awarded to organizations located in New York City.

Typical grant range: $10,000 to $75,000

450
The Barker Welfare Foundation
P.O. Box 2
Glen Head, NY 11545
(516) 759-5592

Recording for the Blind; Fidelco Guide Dog Foundation; Lighthouse for the Blind; National Foundation for Teaching Entrepreneurship to Handicapped and Disadvantaged Youth; Association for Retarded Citizens, Inc.; Helen Keller International (program for children); Saint Vincent's Services, Inc. (renovate Mental Health Clinic)

Typical grant range: $2,000 to $10,000

451
The Sandra Atlas Bass & Edythe & Sol G. Atlas Fund, Inc.
185 Great Neck Road
Great Neck, NY 11021
(516) 487-9030

Visually impaired; physically disabled; Guide Dog Foundation for the Blind; American Printing House for the Blind

Grants awarded to organizations located in New York City and Long Island.

Typical grant range: $2,000 to $25,000

452
Bethesda Foundation, Inc.
P.O. Box 296
North Hornell, NY 14843
(607) 324-1616

Visually impaired; mentally disabled; Howard Public Library (large print books for people who are visually impaired)

Grants awarded to organizations located in the Hornell vicinity.

453
The Bodman Foundation
767 Third Avenue, 4th Floor
New York, NY 10017
(212) 644-0322

Lincoln Center for the Performing Arts (program for youth with disabilities); Goddard Riverside Community Center (career and college counseling for youth with disabilities); Metropolitan Opera Association (tickets for people with disabilities); Animal Medical Center (guide dog program); Triform Camphill Community (job training program for people who are physically disabled)

Grants awarded to organizations located in the New York City vicinity.

Typical grant range: $15,000 to $50,000

454
The Albert C. Bostwick Foundation
Hillside Avenue and Bacon Road
P.O. Box A
Old Westbury, NY 11568
(516) 334-5566

Eye research; physically disabled; National Center for Disability Services

Typical grant range: $1,000 to $25,000

455
Gladys Brooks Foundation
226 Seventh Street, Suite 101
Garden City, NY 11530
(516) 746-6103

Visually impaired; physically disabled; Helen Keller Services for the Blind

Typical grant range: $10,000 to $100,000

456
Central New York Community Foundation, Inc.
500 S. Salina Street, Suite 428
Syracuse, NY 13202
(315) 422-9538

Learning Disabilities Association (program for children who are learning disabled); Centers for Nature Education, Inc. (wheelchair accessibility project); Mental Health Association (program for parents going through a divorce); Onondaga Free Library (audio and large-print books for patrons who are visually impaired)

Grants awarded to organizations located in Onondaga and Madison Counties.

457
Chautauqua Region Community Foundation, Inc.
418 Spring Street
Jamestown, NY 14701-5332
(716) 661-3390

Chautauqua Blind Association, Inc. (education project); Joyce Richards Shelgren Trust to Assist and Aid Needy (program for children who are disabled)

Grants awarded to organizations located in southern Chautauqua County.

Typical grant range: $1,000 to $9,000

458
Liz Claiborne Foundation
1441 Broadway
New York, NY 10018
(212) 626-5704

Physically disabled; March of Dimes Birth Defects Foundation

Grants awarded to organizations located in areas of company operations (Liz Claiborne, Inc.).

Typical grant range: $1,500 to $20,000

459
The Clark Foundation
1 Rockefeller Plaza, 31st Floor
New York, NY 10020
(212) 977-6900

Physically disabled; National Theater Workshop of the Handicapped

Most grants awarded to organizations located in New York City and in Cooperstown, New York.

Typical grant range: $15,000 to $125,000

460
Robert Sterling Clark Foundation, Inc.
135 East 64th Street
New York, NY 10021
(212) 288-8900

Public Advocate for the City of New York (services for people who are mentally ill); State Communities Aid Association (program to enhance children's access to mental health services)

Typical grant range: $10,000 to $80,000

461
The Community Foundation for the Capital Region, N.Y.
Executive Park Drive
Albany, NY 12203
(518) 446-9638

Physically disabled; developmentally disabled; Northeastern Association of the Blind; Easter Seal Society (summer program for children); Daughters of Sarah Nursing Center (accessibility project); Warriors on Wheels (recreation program for people with disabilities); Stride, Inc. (camping program for children with disabilities); Bethlehem Public Library (American Sign Language classes)

Grants awarded to organizations located in Albany, Rensselaer, Saratoga and Schenectady Counties.

Typical grant range: $8,000 to $35,000

462

The Community Foundation of Herkimer and Oneida Counties, Inc.
270 Genesee Street
Utica, NY 13502
(315) 735-8212

Physically and mentally disabled; Special Olympics; Canine Working Companions; Central Association for the Blind and Visually Impaired; Holland Patent Central School District (program to assist children with learning and behavioral problems)

Grants awarded to organizations located in Oneida and Herkimer Counties.

463

The Frances L. & Edwin L. Cummings Memorial Fund
501 Fifth Avenue, Suite 708
New York, NY 10017
(212) 286-1778

Physically disabled; mental health; speech impaired

Grants awarded to organizations located in the New York City vicinity.

Typical grant range: $1,500 to $40,000

464

James H. Cummings Foundation, Inc.
1807 Elmwood Avenue, Suite 112
Buffalo, NY 14207
(716) 874-0040

Learning Disabilities Association; Blind Association; Lothlorien Therapeutic Riding Center, Inc.

Typical grant range: $1,000 to $40,000

465

The Nathan Cummings Foundation, Inc.
1926 Broadway, Suite 600
New York, NY 10023
(212) 787-7300

Physically disabled; developmentally disabled; emotionally disturbed; mental health; National Foundation for Teaching Entrepreneurship to Disadvantaged and Handicapped Youth

Typical grant range: $5,000 to $75,000

466

Dr. G. Clifford & Florence B. Decker Foundation
c/o Galleria
8 Hawley Street
Binghamton, NY 13901
(607) 722-0211

Disabled Sports USA; Association for Retarded Citizens; Challenger Little League of the Southern Tier (building funds for an accessible baseball field)

Grants awarded to organizations located in Broome County.

467

Cleveland H. Dodge Foundation, Inc.
670 W. 247th Street
Bronx, NY 10471
(718) 543-1220

Riverdale Mental Health Association; Springfield College (U.S. Fitness Center for the Disabled)

Most grants awarded to organizations located in New York City.

Typical grant range: $2,000 to $100,000

468

Jean and Louis Dreyfus Foundation, Inc.
c/o Decker Hubbard and Welden Sweeney
30 Rockefeller Plaza, Suite 4340
New York, NY 10112
(212) 218-7575

International Center for the Disabled (Pediatric Mental Health Project)

Grants awarded to organizations located in New York City.

469

Blanche T. Enders Charitable Trust
c/o The Chase Manhattan Bank, N.A.
270 Park Avenue, 21st Floor
New York, NY 10017

Physically disabled; visually impaired

Grants awarded to organizations located in New York City.

Typical grant range: $1,000 to $10,000

470

The Rosamond Gifford Charitable Corporation
518 James Street, Suite 280
Syracuse, NY 13203
(315) 474-2489

Physically disabled; United Cerebral Palsy and Handicapped Children's Association

Grants awarded to organizations located in Onondaga County and Syracuse.

Typical grant range: $5,000 to $50,000

471

The Glens Falls Foundation
237 Glen Street
Glens Falls, NY 12801
(518) 792-1151

Physically disabled; youth; Sabah, Inc. (equipment for skaters with disabilities)

Grants awarded to organizations located in Warren, Washington, and Saratoga Counties.

472

Herman Goldman Foundation
61 Broadway, 18th Floor
New York, NY 10006
(212) 797-9090

Mentally and physically disabled; mental health; visually impaired; youth

Grants awarded to organizations located in the New York City vicinity.

Typical grant range: $5,000 to $40,000

473

William T. Grant Foundation
570 Lexington Avenue, 18th Floor
New York, NY 10022
(212) 752-0071

Mental health; developmentally disabled; research

Typical grant range: $15,000 to $250,000

474

Stella and Charles Guttman Foundation, Inc.
445 Park Avenue, 19th Floor
New York, NY 10022
(212) 371-7082

Physically disabled; mental health; Resources for Children with Special Needs

Grants awarded to organizations located in the New York City vicinity.

Typical grant range: $3,000 to $30,000

475

Hasbro Children's Foundation
32 W. 23rd Street
New York, NY 10010
(212) 645-2400

Physically disabled; youth; Very Special Arts

Typical grant range: $10,000 to $75,000

476

Charles Hayden Foundation
One Bankers Trust Plaza
130 Liberty Street
New York, NY 10006
(212) 938-0790

Mental health; visually impaired; Jewish Board of Family and Children's Services (renovate Mental Health Center)

Typical grant range: $10,000 to $125,000

477

The Hearst Foundation, Inc.
888 Seventh Avenue, 45th Floor
New York, NY 10106
(212) 586-5404

Physically and mentally disabled; United Cerebral Palsy

Typical grant range: $10,000 to $50,000

478

The Heckscher Foundation for Children
17 E. 47th Street
New York, NY 10017
(212) 371-7775

Mentally disabled; visually impaired; hearing impaired; Jewish Guild for the Blind

Most grants awarded to organizations located in the New York City vicinity.

Typical grant range: $1,000 to $30,000

479

The F.B. Heron Foundation
100 Broadway, 17th Floor
New York, NY 10005
(212) 404-1835

Physically disabled; National Multiple Sclerosis Society

Typical grant range: $10,000 to $100,000

480

Ittleson Foundation, Inc.
15 East 67th Street, 5th Floor
New York, NY 10021
(212) 794-2008

Mental health; emotionally disabled; Development for the Disabled, Inc. (housing program for people who are mentally ill)

481

The JM Foundation
60 E. 42nd Street, Room 1651
New York, NY 10165
(212) 687-7735

International Center for the Disabled; American Association of People with Disabilities; Association for the Help of Retarded Children (employment program for people with developmental disabilities); Disabilities and Possibilities Foundation (television program on issues about people who are disabled); National Organization on Disability (Start on Success Student Internship Program); Fearless Theater Company (program for people who are disabled); Gallaudet University (employment program for students who are hearing-impaired)

Typical grant range: $2,500 to $25,000

482

Daisy Marquis Jones Foundation
1600 South Avenue, Suite 250
Rochester, NY 14620
(716) 461-4950

Hearing impaired; mentally and physically disabled; Hearing and Speech Center (grant to help purchase a mobile hearing testing clinic)

Grants awarded to organizations located in Monroe and Yates Counties.

Typical grant range: $2,000 to $30,000

483

The Esther A. & Joseph Klingenstein Fund, Inc.
787 Seventh Avenue, 6th Floor
New York, NY 10019
(212) 492-6181

Physically disabled; National Foundation for Teaching Entrepreneurship to Disadvantaged and Handicapped Youth

Typical grant range: $15,000 to $75,000

484
Loews Foundation
655 Madison Avenue
New York, NY 10021-8043
(212) 521-2416

Physically disabled; hearing impaired;
Children's Hearing Institute

Typical grant range: $2,000 to $25,000

485
Leon Lowenstein Foundation, Inc.
126 East 56th Street, 28th Floor
New York, NY 10022
(212) 319-0670

Visually impaired; Hadley School for the
Blind

Grants awarded to organizations located
in the New York City vicinity.

486
Josiah Macy, Jr. Foundation
44 E. 64th Street
New York, NY 10021
(212) 486-2424

Virginia Foundation for the Exceptional
Child and Adolescent (program to help
people who are developmentally
disabled); The George Washington
University (Center for the Study and
Advancement of Disability Policy)

Typical grant range: $10,000 to $200,000

487
**Merrill Lynch & Company
Foundation, Inc.**
World Financial Center
South Tower, 6th Floor
New York, NY 10080
(212) 236-4319

Hearing impaired; physically disabled;
National Association of the Deaf

Typical grant range: $2,000 to $60,000

488
Metropolitan Life Foundation
One Madison Avenue
New York, NY 10010
(212) 578-6272

Special Olympics; Very Special Arts;
Hearing Society; Resources for Children
with Special Needs; Hadley School for the
Blind

Typical grant range: $1,000 to $100,000

489
**Morgan Stanley Dean Witter
Foundation**
1221 Avenue of the Americas, 27th Floor
New York, NY 10020
(212) 703-4000

Mentally and physically disabled; Young
Adult Institute (program for children who
are developmentally disabled)

Grants awarded to organizations located
in the New York City vicinity.

Typical grant range: $5,000 to $25,000

490
NEC Foundation of America
Eight Corporate Center Drive
Melville, NY 11747
(516) 753-7021

United Cerebral Palsy; Institute for Deaf
and Blind; VSA (arts festival for people
who are disabled); Syracuse University
(technology program for people who are
disabled); American Association for the
Advancement of Science (production of a
video on mentoring students with
disabilities for careers in technology)

Typical grant range: $10,000 to $50,000

491

The New York Times Company Foundation, Inc.
229 W. 43rd Street
New York, NY 10036
(212) 556-1091

Physically disabled; visually impaired; learning disabled; youth; cultural programs; American Foundation for the Blind

Most grants awarded to organizations located in New York City.

Typical grant range: $2,500 to $25,000

492

Northern New York Community Foundation, Inc.
120 Washington Street
Watertown, NY 13601
(315) 782-7110

Physically disabled; Disabled Persons Action Organization

Grants awarded to organizations located in Jefferson and Lewis Counties.

493

The John R. Oishei Foundation
One HSBC Center, Suite 3650
Buffalo, NY 14203
(716) 856-9491

Blind Association of Western New York; Learning Disabilities Association (program for youth); Hearing & Speech Center (Cochlear Implant Program for children); The Children's Guild (care and rehabilitation for children with special needs)

Grants awarded to organizations located in the Buffalo vicinity.

494

Moses L. Parshelsky Foundation
26 Court Street, Suite 904
Brooklyn, NY 11242
(718) 875-8883

Helen Keller Services for the Blind; Jewish Guild for the Blind

Grants awarded to organizations located in Queens and Brooklyn.

495

The Pinkerton Foundation
630 Fifth Avenue, Suite 1755
New York, NY 10111
(212) 332-3385

Mentally and physically disabled; learning disabled; youth; The Learning Disabilities Association

Grants awarded to organizations located in New York City.

Typical grant range: $10,000 to $50,000

496

The Louis and Harold Price Foundation, Inc.
450 Park Avenue, Suite 1102
New York, NY 10022
(212) 753-0240

Visually impaired; youth; Multiple Sclerosis Society; Blind Children's Center

Typical grant range: $1,500 to $20,000

497

Rochester Area Community Foundation
500 East Avenue
Rochester, NY 14607
(716) 271-4100

Learning Disabilities Association; Association for the Blind and Visually Impaired; New York State Association of Self-Help for Hard-of-Hearing People; Rochester Early Childhood Assessment Partnership (mental health project); Wayne ARC Roosevelt Children's Center (special education program); De-Paul Cornerstone (residential facility for adults with mental illness); Nazareth College Speech/Language Pathology Department (video system to help clients who are speech impaired)

Grants awarded in the following counties: Monroe, Genesee, Livingston, Ontario, Orleans and Wayne.

498

Helena Rubinstein Foundation, Inc.
477 Madison Avenue, 7th Floor
New York, NY 10022
(212) 750-7310

Physically disabled; visually impaired;
youth

Grants awarded to organizations located
in New York City.

Typical grant range: $3,000 to $30,000

499

**The Fan Fox and Leslie R. Samuels
Foundation, Inc.**
350 Fifth Avenue, Suite 4301
New York, NY 10118
(212) 239-3030

Jewish Association for Services for the
Aged (mental health services); Theatre
Development Fund, Inc. (program for
theatergoers who are hearing impaired);
The New York Hospital (program for
children who are developmentally
disabled)

Most grants awarded to organizations
located in New York City.

Typical grant range: $5,000 to $100,000

500

The Scherman Foundation, Inc.
16 E. 52nd Street, Suite 601
New York, NY 10022
(212) 832-3086

The National Theatre of the Deaf;
Coalition of Institutionalized Aged and
Disabled

Most grants awarded to organizations
located in New York City.

Typical grant range: $10,000 to $60,000

501

Ralph C. Sheldon Foundation, Inc.
P.O. Box 417
Jamestown, NY 14702
(716) 664-9890

Physically disabled; visually impaired;
Little Theatre (accessible rest room)

Most grants awarded to organizations
located in southern Chautauqua County.

Typical grant range: $12,000 to $55,000

502

**The Seth Sprague Educational and
Charitable Foundation**
c/o U.S. Trust Co. of New York
114 W. 47th Street
New York, NY 10036
(212) 852-3683

Physically disabled; visually impaired;
American Association of People with
Disabilities

503

St. Giles Foundation
420 Lexington Avenue, Suite 1641
New York, NY 10170
(212) 338-9001

Physically disabled; education; Saint Hildas
and Saint Hughs School (scholarship
program for students who are disabled)

Typical grant range: $15,000 to $150,000

504

van Ameringen Foundation, Inc.
509 Madison Avenue
New York, NY 10022
(212) 758-6221

Mental health; mentally and physically
disabled; visually impaired; Association to
Benefit Children (Mobile Mental Health
Team)

Typical grant range: $20,000 to $60,000

505
The Margaret L. Wendt Foundation
40 Fountain Plaza, Suite 277
Buffalo, NY 14202
(716) 855-2146

Physically disabled; mental health;
visually impaired; accessibility project;
Alliance for the Mentally Ill

Most grants awarded to organizations
located in the Buffalo vicinity.

Typical grant range: $5,000 to $100,000

506
The Western New York Foundation
Main Seneca Building, Suite 1402
237 Main Street
Buffalo, NY 14203
(716) 847-6440

Physically disabled; accessibility project

Grants awarded to organizations located
in western New York State (Allegany,
Cattaraugus, Chautauqua, Erie, Genesee,
Niagara, and Wyoming Counties).

Typical grant range: $2,000 to $20,000

NORTH CAROLINA

507
Bank of America Foundation
401 N. Tryon Street, NC1-007-18-01
Charlotte, NC 28255

Foundation for the Junior Blind; Family
Alliance for the Mentally Ill; International
Guiding Eyes Foundation; Optimist
Foundation for Handicapped Children;
Association of Retarded Children and
Adults; A Touch of Understanding, Inc.
(education programs about people who are
disabled); Goodwill Industries (vocational
training and placement programs)

Grants awarded to organizations located
in areas of company operations (Bank of
America Corp.).

508
The Cannon Foundation, Inc.
P.O. Box 548
Concord, NC 28026
(704) 786-8216

Visually impaired; mentally disabled;
National Society to Prevent Blindness

Grants awarded to organizations located
in North Carolina, with an emphasis in
Cabarrus County.

Typical grant range: $10,000 to $100,000

509
The Cemala Foundation, Inc.
122 N. Elm Street, Suite 816
Greensboro, NC 27401
(336) 274-3541

Mentally and physically disabled;
independent living program; Learning
Disabilities Association; Special
Olympics; Prevent Blindness; Goodwill
Industries Rehabilitation Center
(employment program)

Most grants awarded to organizations
located in Guilford County.

Typical grant range: $5,000 to $60,000

510
**The Community Foundation of
Henderson County, Inc.**
Fourth Avenue and Main Street
P.O. Box 1108
Hendersonville, NC 28793
(704) 697-6224

Special Olympics; March of Dimes;
National Multiple Sclerosis Society;
Trend Mental Health (purchase tricycle);
Peninsula Village (mental health treatment
program)

Grants awarded to organizations located
in Henderson County.

511
The Duke Endowment
100 N. Tryon Street, Suite 3500
Charlotte, NC 28202
(704) 376-0291

Physically disabled; developmentally disabled; youth; Brownings Church (accessibility project); Carobell Children's Home (building funds for a rehabilitation facility for people who are disabled); Lutheran Family Services (group home for people who are physically disabled or autistic)

Typical grant range: $25,000 to $150,000

512
Durham Merchants Association Charitable Foundation
P. O. Box 52016
Durham, NC 27717
(919) 489-7921

Visually impaired; Special Olympics; Prevent Blindness

Grants awarded to organizations located in the Durham vicinity.

Typical grant range: $500 to $7,000

513
Foundation for the Carolinas
P.O. Box 34769
Charlotte, NC 28234
(704) 376-9541

Mentally and physically disabled

Most grants awarded to organizations located in North Carolina and South Carolina.

514
The Glaxo Wellcome Foundation
Five Moore Drive
Research Triangle Park, NC 27709
(919) 483-2140

Visually impaired; mentally disabled; Recording for the Blind

Grants awarded to organizations located in North Carolina.

515
Kate B. Reynolds Charitable Trust
128 Reynolda Village
Winston-Salem, NC 27106
(336) 723-1456

North Carolina Alliance for the Mentally Ill, Inc.; Guilford Advocacy Project for the Handicapped; Association for the Blind and Visually Impaired, Inc.; County Council on Aging (purchase hearing aids); Eastern North Carolina School for the Deaf Foundation, Inc. (technology program for students who are deaf or physically disabled); Macon Citizens for the Handicapped, Inc. (fitness center for people who are disabled); North Carolina State University (home accessibility project for people who are disabled); RSI Transitional Group Home, Inc. (group home facility for adults who are developmentally disabled); Western Carolina Center Foundation, Inc. (dental treatment program for people who are mentally retarded/developmentally disabled)

Grants awarded to organizations located in North Carolina.

Typical grant range: $20,000 to $200,000

516
Z. Smith Reynolds Foundation, Inc.
101 Reynolda Village
Winston-Salem, NC 27106
(336) 725-7541

Physically disabled; Tri-County Industries (educate companies about the self-reliance of people with disabilities)

Grants awarded to organizations located in North Carolina.

Typical grant range: $15,000 to $75,000

517

The Winston-Salem Foundation
860 W. 5th Street
Winston-Salem, NC 27101
(336) 725-2382

Developmentally disabled; mentally disabled; The Special Children's School (program for children who are developmentally disabled)

Most grants awarded to organizations located in Forsyth County.

Typical grant range: $1,000 to $25,000

NORTH DAKOTA

518

Tom and Frances Leach Foundation, Inc.
P.O. Box 1136
Bismarck, ND 58502
(701) 255-0479

Physically disabled

Most grants awarded to organizations located in North Dakota.

Typical grant range: $2,000 to $30,000

OHIO

519

Akron Community Foundation
345 W. Cedar Street
Akron, OH 44307
(330) 376-8522

Civic Theatre (rest room accessibility program); Akron Rotary Foundation (playground for students who are physically disabled); Akron Cuyahoga Valley Preservation & Scenic Railway Association (accessible car); Vision Rehabilitation (independent living program for adults who are blind)

Most grants awarded to organizations located in the Akron vicinity.

Typical grant range: $1,000 to $20,000

520

Bicknell Fund
c/o Advisory Services, Inc.
1422 Euclid Avenue, Suite 1010
Cleveland, OH 44115
(216) 363-6482

National Multiple Sclerosis Society; Cleveland Hearing & Speech Center; Cleveland Sight Center; Therapeutic Riding Center, Inc.

Most grants awarded to organizations located in the Cleveland vicinity.

Typical grant range: $1,500 to $10,000

521

Britton Fund
1422 Euclid Avenue, Room 1010
Cleveland, OH 44115
(216) 363-6489

Therapeutic Riding Center, Inc.; Cleveland Hearing & Speech Center; Cleveland Sight Center

Grants awarded to organizations located in Ohio.

522

Eva L. and Joseph M. Bruening Foundation
1422 Euclid Avenue, Suite 627
Cleveland, OH 44115
(216) 621-2632

United Cerebral Palsy; Goodwill Industries (literacy project for people who are mentally disabled or developmentally disabled); Cleveland San Jose Ballet (program for students with disabilities); Vocational Guidance Services (program for people who are disabled to become more independent)

Grants awarded to organizations located in Cuyahoga County.

Typical grant range: $5,000 to $65,000

523

The George W. Codrington Charitable Foundation
c/o Key Trust Company of Ohio, N.A.
P.O. Box 5937
Cleveland, OH 44101
(216) 566-5837

Society for the Blind; Hearing and Speech Center; United Cerebral Palsy

Grants awarded to organizations located in Cuyahoga County.

524

Columbus Medical Association Foundation
431 E. Broad Street
Columbus, OH 43215-3820
(614) 240-7420

Fairfield Center for Disabilities and Cerebral Palsy, Inc.; Columbus Montessori Education Center (program for children who are developmentally disabled); YMCA (elevator accessibility project); Children's Hospital (Community Collaboration for Visually Impaired Children)

Grants awarded to organizations located in Franklin County.

525

The Community Foundation of Greater Lorain County
1865 N. Ridge Road East, Suite A
Lorain, OH 44055
(440) 277-0142

Lorain County Metro Parks (accessibility project); Linking Employment, Ability and Potential/Center for Independent Living (Disability Information Access Network); Our Lady of the Wayside (music therapy program for people who are developmentally disabled or physically disabled)

Grants awarded to organizations located in the Lorain County vicinity.

Typical grant range: $2,000 to $25,000

526

Coshocton Foundation
P.O. Box 55
Coshocton, OH 43812
(614) 622-0010

Board of Mental Retardation; March of Dimes; Six County Mental Health; Residential Homes for the Developmentally Disabled (accessible transit bus)

Grants awarded to organizations located in Coshocton County.

Typical grant range: $1,000 to $10,000

527

Charles H. Dater Foundation, Inc.
602 Main Street, Suite 302
Cincinnati, OH 45202
(513) 241-1234

Saint Rita School for the Deaf; Cincinnati Speech and Hearing Center; Cincinnati Riding for the Handicapped; Northern Kentucky Association for the Retarded; Easter Seals (speech program for children); Cincinnati Association for the Blind (lending library for children who are visually impaired)

Grants awarded to organizations located in the Cincinnati vicinity.

Typical grant range: $1,000 to $15,000

528

The Dayton Foundation
2100 Kettering Tower
Dayton, OH 45423
(937) 222-0410

Mentally and physically disabled; developmentally disabled; Disabled Consumers Network (program for people who are visually impaired); Legal Assistance Foundation (services for families with children who are disabled); Volunteer Caregivers of Life Essentials, Inc. (program for people who are mentally and physically disabled)

Most grants awarded to organizations located in the Dayton vicinity.

529
The Eaton Charitable Fund
Eaton Corporation
1111 Superior Avenue
Cleveland, OH 44114
(216) 523-4438

Therapeutic Riding Center; Goodwill
Industries; National Center for Learning
Disabilities

Grants awarded to organizations located
in areas of company operations (Eaton
Corp.).

Typical grant range: $1,000 to $11,000

530
The 1525 Foundation
1111 Superior Avenue, Suite 1000
Cleveland, OH 44114
(216) 696-4200

Goodwill Industries; Recording for the
Blind and Dyslexic

Most grants awarded to organizations
located in Cuyahoga County.

Typical grant range: $5,000 to $75,000

531
The GAR Foundation
50 S. Main Street
P.O. Box 1500
Akron, OH 44309-1500
(330) 643-0201

Visually impaired; mentally and
physically disabled

Typical grant range: $5,000 to $50,000

532
The Greater Cincinnati Foundation
300 W. 4th Street, Suite 200
Cincinnati, OH 45202
(513) 241-2880

Dyslexia; Cincinnati Association for the
Blind; Special Olympics; United Cerebral
Palsy; St. Rita School for the Deaf; Radio
Reading Services of Greater Cincinnati;
Home of Mercy Environment (home
health care for people who are disabled);
St. Joseph Children's Treatment Center
(mental health services); Tender Mercies
(housing for people who are mentally ill);
Prevent Blindness Ohio (vision care
program)

Grants awarded to organizations located
in the Cincinnati vicinity.

Typical grant range: $2,500 to $50,000

533
The George Gund Foundation
1845 Guildhall Building
45 Prospect Avenue West
Cleveland, OH 44115
(216) 241-3114

Physically disabled; visually impaired;
Cleveland Public Schools (special
education project)

Most grants awarded to organizations
located in the Cleveland vicinity.

Typical grant range: $5,000 to $150,000

534
**George M. and Pamela S. Humphrey
Fund**
c/o Advisory Services, Inc.
1422 Euclid Avenue, Suite 1010
Cleveland, OH 44115
(216) 363-6483

Visually impaired; hearing impaired;
Seeing Eye Dog, Inc.

Grants awarded to organizations located
in Ohio.

Typical grant range: $2,000 to $20,000

535

The Invacare Foundation
899 Cleveland Street
Elyria, OH 44035
(440) 329-6000

Physically disabled

Grants awarded to organizations located in Ohio.

536

The Martha Holden Jennings Foundation
710 Halle Building
1228 Euclid Avenue
Cleveland, OH 44115
(216) 589-5700

Cleveland Society for the Blind; United Cerebral Palsy Association of Greater Cleveland, Inc.; Ohio Association for Protection & Advocacy for Persons with Developmental Disabilities; Cleveland Public Schools (Special Olympics program); Cleveland Signstage Theater, Inc. (education outreach program)

Grants awarded to organizations located in Ohio.

Typical grant range: $5,000 to $200,000

537

The Lubrizol Foundation
29400 Lakeland Blvd., Suite 53A
Wickliffe, OH 44092
(440) 943-4200

Cleveland Sight Center; Goodwill Industries; Cleveland Hearing & Speech Center

Grants awarded to organizations located in areas of company operations (The Lubrizol Corp.).

Typical grant range: $2,000 to $25,000

538

Manuel D. & Rhoda Mayerson Foundation
312 Walnut Street, Suite 3600
Cincinnati, OH 45202
(513) 621-7500

Multiple Sclerosis Society; Cincinnati Speech and Hearing Center; Disability Rights Education and Defense Fund; Radio Reading Services; Capabilities Unlimited, Inc. (program for people who are developmentally disabled); Cincinnati Music Hall (accessibility project); Joy Outdoor Education Center (accessibility project for people who are physically disabled)

Most grants awarded to organizations located in Cincinnati.

539

The Harry C. Moores Foundation
Bricker and Eckler
100 S. Third Street
Columbus, OH 43215
(614) 227-8884

Physically and mentally disabled; visually impaired; rehabilitation; Goodwill Industries

Most grants awarded to organizations located in the Columbus vicinity.

Typical grant range: $5,000 to $50,000

540

The Burton D. Morgan Foundation
P.O. Box 1500
Akron, OH 44309
(330) 258-6512

Mental health; Alliance for the Mentally Ill

Typical grant range: $5,000 to $100,000

541

John P. Murphy Foundation
Tower City Center
Suite 924 Terminal Tower
50 Public Square
Cleveland, OH 44113
(216) 623-4770

Physically disabled; hearing impaired;
Therapeutic Riding Center

Grants awarded to organizations located
in the Cleveland vicinity.

Typical grant range: $5,000 to $50,000

542

Nationwide Foundation
One Nationwide Plaza
Columbus, OH 43215
(614) 249-5095

Physically disabled; visually impaired;
Goodwill Industries; Alliance for the
Mentally Ill

Grants awarded to organizations located
in areas of company operations
(Nationwide Mutual Insurance Co.), with
an emphasis in Columbus.

Typical grant range: $2,500 to $50,000

543

The Nord Family Foundation
347 Midway Blvd., Suite 312
Elyria, OH 44035
(440) 324-2822

The Nord Community Mental Health
Center; Lorain County Board of Mental
Retardation & Developmental Disabilities;
Lorain County Safe Harbor/Genesis
House (shelter and support for women
with disabilities); St. Mary Academy
(equipment for students who are hearing
impaired); Cornucopia, Inc. (job training
program for people who are disabled);
Case Western Reserve University (Mental
Health Research Institute)

Grants awarded to organizations located
in Cuyahoga and Lorain Counties.

Typical grant range: $5,000 to $50,000

544

The Nordson Corporation Foundation
28601 Clemens Road
Westlake, OH 44145
(440) 892-1580

Physically disabled; mental health;
learning disabled; special education;
Cleveland Hearing and Speech Center;
National Multiple Sclerosis Society (peer
counseling program)

Typical grant range: $3,000 to $50,000

545

**The William J. and Dorothy K. O'Neill
Foundation, Inc.**
30195 Chagrin Blvd., Suite 310
Cleveland, OH 44124
(216) 831-9667

Cleveland Sight Center; Center for Mental
Retardation; Fairfield Regional Vision
Rehabilitation Center; Special Olympics
(ski equipment repair); Templum (mental
health program)

Typical grant range: $2,500 to $25,000

546

Ohio Valley Foundation
c/o Fifth Third Bank
38 Fountain Square Plaza
Mail Drop 1090 D7
Cincinnati, OH 45263
(513) 579-6034

Cincinnati Riding for the Handicapped
(equipment)

Grants awarded to organizations located
in the Cincinnati vicinity.

547

The Elisabeth Severance Prentiss Foundation
c/o National City Bank
1900 E. 9th Street, LOC-2066
Cleveland, OH 44114
(216) 575-2760

United Cerebral Palsy; Therapeutic Riding Center, Inc.; Achievement Centers for Children (services for children with disabilities); Psychobiology Clinic (mental health treatment program)

Grants awarded to organizations located in the Cleveland vicinity.

Typical grant range: $25,000 to $100,000

548

The Helen Steiner Rice Foundation
221 E. Fourth Street, Suite 2100, Atrium 2
P.O. Box 0236
Cincinnati, OH 45201
(513) 451-9241

Physically disabled; developmentally disabled; youth

Grants awarded to organizations located in Lorain, Ohio and the Cincinnati vicinity.

549

Richland County Foundation
24 W. Third Street, Suite 100
Mansfield, OH 44902
(419) 525-3020

Independent Living Center; Mansfield Richland County Public Library (talking books); Camp Nuhop (camp for children with special needs); John Simpson Middle School (Deaf Theater); Clear Fork Valley School (life skills program for students who are multi-disabled)

Grants awarded to organizations located in Richland County.

550

The Samuel Rosenthal Foundation
c/o Foundation Management Services
1422 Euclid Avenue, Suite 627
Cleveland, OH 44115
(216) 696-7273

United Cerebral Palsy; Park Synagogue (accessible rest rooms); Deafness Research Foundation (speech program); National Multiple Sclerosis Society (Respite Care Program)

Grants awarded to organizations located in the Cleveland vicinity.

Typical grant range: $2,000 to $50,000

551

Albert G. and Olive H. Schlink Foundation
49 Benedict Avenue, Suite C
Norwalk, OH 44857-2161
(419) 668-8211

Toledo Sight Center; Prevent Blindness; Cleveland Sight Center

Most grants awarded to organizations located in Ohio.

Typical grant range: $5,000 to $35,000

552

Scripps Howard Foundation
P.O. Box 5380
Cincinnati, OH 45201
(513) 977-3035

Northern Kentucky Association for the Retarded; Prevent Blindness; Canine Companions for Independence; National Multiple Sclerosis Society; Radio Reading Services; St. Rita School for the Deaf

Typical grant range: $1,000 to $10,000

553

The Sisler McFawn Foundation
P.O. Box 149
Akron, OH 44309
(330) 849-8887

Physically disabled; Old Trail School
(accessible elevator); Mental Health
Association (adolescent suicide
prevention program)

Grants awarded to organizations located
in Summit County.

Typical grant range: $1,000 to $15,000

554

**The Kelvin and Eleanor Smith
Foundation**
26380 Curtiss Wright Parkway, Suite 105
Cleveland, OH 44143
(216) 289-5789

Visually impaired; Cleveland Society for
the Blind

Grants awarded to organizations located
in the Cleveland vicinity.

Typical grant range: $5,000 to $125,000

555

Star Bank, N.A., Foundation
P.O. Box 1038
Cincinnati, OH 45201
(513) 632-4000

Mentally and physically disabled

Most grants awarded to organizations
located in the Cincinnati vicinity.

Typical grant range: $1,000 to $50,000

556

The Stranahan Foundation
4159 Holland-Sylvania Road, Suite 206
Toledo, OH 43623
(419) 882-6575

Toledo Society for the Blind-The Sight
Center; Assistance Dogs of America, Inc.
(dog training program to help people with
special needs); Adopt America Network
(adoptive agency for children with special
needs); Bittersweet Farms (education,
vocation, and social needs program for
people with autism)

Most grants awarded to organizations
located in the Toledo vicinity.

Typical grant range: $2,000 to $50,000

557

Toledo Community Foundation, Inc.
608 Madison Avenue, Suite 1540
Toledo, OH 43604
(419) 241-5049

Toledo Society for the Blind; Assistance
Dogs of America, Inc.

Most grants awarded to organizations
located in the Toledo vicinity.

558

The Thomas H. White Foundation
1422 Euclid Avenue, Suite 627
Cleveland, OH 44115
(216) 696-7273

Physically disabled; Cleveland Hearing &
Speech Center

Grants awarded to organizations located
in Cuyahoga County.

Typical grant range: $1,000 to $12,000

559

Wolfe Associates Inc.
34 S. Third Street
Columbus, OH 43215
(614) 461-5220

Columbus Speech and Hearing Center

Most grants awarded to organizations
located in the Columbus vicinity.

Typical grant range: $1,000 to $20,000

OKLAHOMA

560
The Mervin Bovaird Foundation
100 W. Fifth Street, Suite 800
Tulsa, OK 74103
(918) 583-1777

Physically disabled; speech impaired; hearing impaired; Tulsa Speech and Hearing Association

Most grants awarded to organizations located in the Tulsa vicinity.

Typical grant range: $2,500 to $30,000

561
H.A. and Mary K. Chapman Charitable Trust
6100 South Yale, Suite 1816
Tulsa, OK 74136
(918) 496-7882

Physically disabled; United Cerebral Palsy; Tulsa Speech and Hearing Association

Most grants awarded to organizations located in Tulsa.

Typical grant range: $5,000 to $75,000

562
The J.E. and L.E. Mabee Foundation, Inc.
3000 Mid-Continent Tower
401 South Boston
Tulsa, OK 74103
(918) 584-4286

Physically disabled; visually impaired; Goodwill Industries

Typical grant range: $50,000 to $500,000

563
The Samuel Roberts Noble Foundation, Inc.
2510 Sam Noble Parkway
P.O. Box 2180
Ardmore, OK 73402
(580) 223-5810

Mentally and physically disabled; mental health; Special Olympics

Typical grant range: $5,000 to $100,000

564
Sarkeys Foundation
116 S. Peters, Suite 219
Norman, OK 73069
(405) 364-3703

Mentally and physically disabled; Special Olympics

Grants awarded to organizations located in Oklahoma.

Typical grant range: $5,000 to $80,000

565
The William K. Warren Foundation
P.O. Box 470372
Tulsa, OK 74147
(918) 492-8100

Mental health; physically disabled; Mental Health Association

Most grants awarded to organizations located in Oklahoma.

Typical grant range: $1,000 to $35,000

566
The Maxine and Jack Zarrow Foundation
401 S. Boston, Suite 900
Tulsa, OK 74103
(918) 587-3391

Mental health; Mental Health Association

Grants awarded to organizations located in Tulsa.

Typical grant range: $1,000 to $15,000

567
John Steele Zink Foundation
1259 East 26th Street
Tulsa, OK 74114
(918) 749-8249

Physically disabled; Tulsa Speech and Hearing Association

Grants awarded to organizations located in Oklahoma, with an emphasis in Tulsa.

Typical grant range: $5,000 to $20,000

OREGON

568
The Carpenter Foundation
711 E. Main Street, Suite 10
Medford, OR 97504-7139
(541) 772-5851

Mental health; physically disabled;
Goodwill Industries

Grants awarded to organizations located
in Jackson and Josephine Counties.

Typical grant range: $2,500 to $15,000

569
The Collins Foundation
1618 S.W. First Avenue, Suite 305
Portland, OR 97201
(503) 227-7171

Physically disabled; hearing impaired;
speech impaired; autism; learning
disabled; youth; education; Hearing and
Speech Institute

Grants awarded to organizations located
in Oregon.

Typical grant range: $3,000 to $100,000

570
Leslie G. Ehmann Trust
c/o U.S. National Bank of Oregon
P.O. Box 3168
Portland, OR 97208
(503) 275-5718

Dogs for the Deaf; Dogs for the Blind

Few grants awarded.

Most grants awarded to organizations
located in Oregon.

571
The Ford Family Foundation
P.O. Box 1550
Roseburg, OR 97470
(541) 957-5574

Mentally and physically disabled;
Association for Retarded Citizens

Typical grant range: $10,000 to $150,000

572
Meyer Memorial Trust
1515 S.W. Fifth Avenue, Suite 500
Portland, OR 97201
(503) 228-5512

Physically disabled; mental health;
learning disabled; hearing impaired;
Southern Oregon Goodwill Industries;
Clark Care and Development Center
(program for families with children who
are developmentally disabled)

Most grants awarded to organizations
located in Oregon.

Typical grant range: $5,000 to $75,000

573
The Oregon Community Foundation
621 S.W. Morrison, Suite 725
Portland, OR 97205

Special Olympics; Easter Seal Society;
The Hearing and Speech Institute; Mental
Health Services West; Foundation for the
Blind; United Cerebral Palsy Association;
Shriners Hospital for Crippled Children;
Oregon Lions Sight & Hearing Foundation

Grants awarded to organizations located
in Oregon.

Typical grant range: $5,000 to $50,000

574
Rose E. Tucker Charitable Trust
900 S.W. Fifth Avenue, 24th Floor
Portland, OR 97204
(503) 224-3380

Autistic Children's Activity Program;
Portland Handicapped Artists, Musicians,
& Entertainers, Inc.; Albertina Kerr
Centers (psychiatric residential treatment
facility); Mount Olive School (computer
lab for children who are dyslexic)

Most grants awarded to organizations
located in Oregon, with an emphasis in
the Portland vicinity.

Typical grant range: $2,000 to $15,000

PENNSYLVANIA

575
Alcoa Foundation
201 Isabella Street
Pittsburgh, PA 15212
(412) 553-2348

Mentally and physically disabled; visually impaired; Association for Retarded Citizens

Grants awarded to organizations located in areas of company operations.

Typical grant range: $1,000 to $25,000

576
The Arcadia Foundation
105 E. Logan Street
Norristown, PA 19401
(610) 275-8460

Visually impaired; physically disabled; Association for the Blind

Grants awarded to organizations located in eastern Pennsylvania.

Typical grant range: $2,500 to $25,000

577
The Buhl Foundation
Four Gateway Center, Room 1325
Pittsburgh, PA 15222
(412) 566-2711

Easter Seal Society; United Mental Health, Inc.; Greater Pittsburgh Guild for the Blind; ARC (provide care for adults upon the death of their parents or guardians); George Junior Republic School in Pennsylvania (program for children who are learning disabled); D.T. Watson Rehabilitation Services (public school mainstream program for children with autism)

Most grants awarded to organizations located in southwestern Pennsylvania, with an emphasis in the Pittsburgh vicinity.

Typical grant range: $3,000 to $60,000

578
The Anne L. and George H. Clapp Charitable and Educational Trust
c/o Mellon Bank
Three Mellon Bank Center, Room 4000
Pittsburgh, PA 15259
(412) 234-1634

Western Pennsylvania School for the Deaf; Three Rivers Adoption Council (special needs adoption program)

Grants awarded to organizations located in the Pittsburgh vicinity.

Typical grant range: $5,000 to $15,000

579
Connelly Foundation
One Tower Bridge, Suite 1450
West Conshohocken, PA 19428
(610) 834-3222

Learning disabled; physically disabled; Canine Partners for Life (program for dogs to help people who are disabled)

Grants awarded to organizations located in Philadelphia and the greater Delaware Valley.

Typical grant range: $5,000 to $50,000

580
The Eberly Foundation
P.O. Box 2043
Uniontown, PA 15401
(724) 438-3789

Special Olympics; Spina Bifida Association; Fayette County Association for the Blind

Typical grant range: $10,000 to $200,000

581
The Federation of Independent School Alumnae
1001 Liberty Avenue
Liberty Center, Suite 650
Pittsburgh, PA 15222
(412) 456-5550

Disability Funders Network; ARC Allegheny; Western Pennsylvania School for Blind Children; Advisory Board on Autism and Related Disorders; Goodwill Industries; Western Pennsylvania School for the Deaf; The Washington Hospital Foundation (physical fitness program for children with disabilities); YMCA (building funds for an accessible nature/adventure trail for people with disabilities)

Most grants awarded to organizations located in southwestern Pennsylvania.

Typical grant range: $5,000 to $50,000

582
Grable Foundation
650 Smithfield Street, Suite 240
Pittsburgh, PA 15222
(412) 471-4550

National Alliance for Research on Schizophrenia and Depression; Western Pennsylvania School for the Deaf

Typical grant range: $5,000 to $50,000

583
The Greater Harrisburg Foundation
200 N. 3rd Street, 8th Floor
P.O. Box 678
Harrisburg, PA 17108
(717) 236-5040

Easter Seals; Association for Retarded Citizens; United Cerebral Palsy Center; Susquehanna Art Museum (accessibility project); Marysville-Rye Public Library (books on tape); AHEDD (employment program for youth who are disabled); Alliance for the Mentally Ill (police officer training program for dealing with people who are mentally ill)

Grants awarded to organizations located in the following Counties: Dauphin, Perry, Franklin, Cumberland and Lebanon.

584
H.J. Heinz Company Foundation
P.O. Box 57
Pittsburgh, PA 15230
(412) 456-5772

Mentally and physically disabled; youth; Goodwill Industries

Grants awarded to organizations located in areas of company operations (H.J. Heinz Company).

Typical grant range: $1,000 to $25,000

585
Howard Heinz Endowment
30 CNG Tower
625 Liberty Avenue
Pittsburgh, PA 15222
(412) 281-5777

Western Pennsylvania School for the Deaf

Grants awarded to organizations located in Pennsylvania, with an emphasis in Pittsburgh and southwestern Pennsylvania.

Typical grant range: $25,000 to $250,000

586
Vira I. Heinz Endowment
30 CNG Tower
625 Liberty Avenue
Pittsburgh, PA 15222
(412) 281-5777

Physically disabled; National Foundation for Teaching Entrepreneurship to Disadvantaged and Handicapped Youths, Inc.

Most grants awarded to organizations located in the Pittsburgh vicinity.

Typical grant range: $10,000 to $200,000

587
The Hillman Foundation, Inc.
2000 Grant Building
Pittsburgh, PA 15219
(412) 338-3466

Mental Health Association; D.T. Watson Rehabilitation Services (program for children with autism); The Emmaus Community of Pittsburgh (program for people who are mentally disabled); McGuire Memorial Home Foundation (communication equipment for children who are developmentally disabled); Seton Hill College (special education teacher training program)

Most grants awarded to organizations located in the Pittsburgh vicinity.

Typical grant range: $25,000 to $100,000

588
The Huston Foundation
2 Tower Bridge, Suite 190
1 Fayette Street
Conshohocken, PA 19428
(610) 832-4949

Recording for the Blind and Dyslexic; Dog Guide Users Network; The Little Light House (special education for children with special needs); Main Line Art Center (program for children with special needs); The ARC (program for children who are developmentally disabled); Association for Blind (camp for children who are visually impaired); Baker Industries (employment and rehabilitation program for people who are disabled)

Typical grant range: $2,500 to $30,000

589
The Stewart Huston Charitable Trust
76 S. First Avenue
Coatesville, PA 19320
(610) 384-2666

Physically disabled; visually impaired; accessibility projects; Wheelchair Access, Inc.; Christ the King Lutheran Church of the Deaf; Paoli Presbyterian Church (counseling for children with learning disorders); Easter Seals Society (camp and recreation program for children with disabilities)

Typical grant range: $1,000 to $20,000

590
The Mary Hillman Jennings Foundation
2203 Allegheny Tower
625 Stanwix Street
Pittsburgh, PA 15222
(412) 434-5606

Physically disabled; Allegheny Valley School for Exceptional Children

Most grants awarded to organizations located in the Pittsburgh vicinity.

Typical grant range: $5,000 to $50,000

591
T. James Kavanagh Foundation
P.O. Box 609
Broomall, PA 19008
(610) 356-0743

Keystone Blind Association; Lions Club of South Philadelphia (Christmas party for people who are blind); St. Joseph's School (program for students with special needs); Mercy Community Hospital (purchase wheelchairs)

Typical grant range: $500 to $5,000

592
Josiah W. and Bessie H. Kline Foundation, Inc.
515 S. 29th Street
Harrisburg, PA 17104
(717) 232-0266

Special Olympics; United Cerebral Palsy; Alliance for the Mentally Ill; Easter Seal Society; National Multiple Sclerosis Society; Girl Scout Council (accessibility project)

Grants awarded to organizations located in south central Pennsylvania.

Typical grant range: $1,500 to $25,000

593
Laurel Foundation
Two Gateway Center, Suite 1800
Pittsburgh, PA 15222
(412) 765-2400

Mental Health Association; Pittsburgh Vision Services (employment program for people who are visually impaired)

Typical grant range: $5,000 to $25,000

594
Massey Charitable Trust
P.O. Box 1178
Coraopolis, PA 15108
(412) 262-5992

Mentally and physically disabled; visually impaired; youth; education; Association for Retarded Citizens

Typical grant range: $5,000 to $35,000

595
McCune Foundation
6 PPG Place, Suite 750
Pittsburgh, PA 15222
(412) 644-8779

Physically disabled; visually impaired; youth; accessibility project

Most grants awarded to organizations located in southwestern Pennsylvania, with an emphasis in the Pittsburgh vicinity.

Typical grant range: $50,000 to $300,000

596
Katherine Mabis McKenna Foundation, Inc.
P.O. Box 186
Latrobe, PA 15650
(724) 537-6900

Visually impaired; Association for the Blind

Grants awarded to organizations located in Westmoreland County.

Typical grant range: $2,500 to $50,000

597
John McShain Charities, Inc.
300 E. Lancaster Avenue, Suite 200
Wynnewood, PA 19096-2105

Physically disabled; mental health; visually impaired; Saint Edmonds Home for Crippled Children

Most grants awarded to organizations located in Philadelphia.

Typical grant range: $2,500 to $100,000

598
Mellon Financial Corporation Foundation
One Mellon Bank Center, Suite 1830
Pittsburgh, PA 15258
(412) 234-2732

Mentally and physically disabled; visually impaired; Goodwill Industries

Grants awarded to organizations located in southwestern Pennsylvania.

Typical grant range: $5,000 to $20,000

599
Richard King Mellon Foundation
One Mellon Bank Center
500 Grant Street, Suite 4106
Pittsburgh, PA 15219
(412) 392-2800

Mentally and physically disabled; emotionally disturbed; visually impaired; Association for Retarded Citizens

Most grants awarded to organizations located in the Pittsburgh vicinity.

Typical grant range: $20,000 to $200,000

600

The Pew Charitable Trusts
One Commerce Square
2005 Market Street, Suite 1700
Philadelphia, PA 19103
(215) 575-9050

United Cerebral Palsy Association;
Central Montgomery Mental Health/
Mental Retardation Center; Mental Health
Association; Society for Handicapped
Children and Adults; Gateway
Employment Resources (employment
program for people who are learning
disabled); Network of Victim Assistance
(sexual abuse prevention program for
people with disabilities); Academy of
Community Music, Inc. (music therapy
for children who are mentally or
physically disabled); Special Equestrians
(therapeutic horseback riding for children
with disabilities); Elizabeth Blackwell
Health Center for Women (program
serving women who are developmentally
disabled)

Typical grant range: $100,000 to
$1,000,000

601

The Philadelphia Foundation
1234 Market Street, Suite 1900
Philadelphia, PA 19107
(215) 563-6417

Physically disabled; visually impaired;
youth

Most grants awarded to organizations
located in the Philadelphia vicinity.

Typical grant range: $2,000 to $50,000

602

The Pittsburgh Foundation
One PPG Place, 30th Floor
Pittsburgh, PA 15222
(412) 391-5122

Physically and mentally disabled; learning
disabled; mental health; youth; United
Cerebral Palsy Association

Grants awarded to organizations located
in the Pittsburgh vicinity.

603

PNC Bank Foundation
c/o PNC Bank, N.A.
Fifth Ave. and Wood St., 29th Fl.
Pittsburgh, PA 15222
(412) 762-3137

Mental Health Association; Easter Seal
Society; Goodwill Industries; Multiple
Sclerosis Society; United Cerebral Palsy;
Pittsburgh Blind Association; Somerset
County Blind Center

Grants awarded to organizations located
in areas of company operations (PNC
Bank, N.A.).

Typical grant range: $1,500 to $20,000

604

PPG Industries Foundation
One PPG Place
Pittsburgh, PA 15272
(412) 434-2962

Mentally and physically disabled; visually
impaired; Association for Retarded
Citizens; Pittsburgh Blind Association

Grants awarded to organizations located
in areas of company operations (PPG
Industries, Inc.), with an emphasis in
Pittsburgh.

Typical grant range: $500 to $25,000

605

Herbert M. Rehmeyer Trust
c/o The York Bank & Trust Co.
21 E. Market Street
York, PA 17401
(717) 846-9800

Mentally disabled; mental health;
Association of Retarded Citizens

Grants awarded to organizations located
in York County.

Typical grant range: $1,000 to $10,000

606

Scaife Family Foundation
1 Oxford Centre
301 Grant Street, Suite 3900
Pittsburgh, PA 15219
(412) 392-2900

Physically disabled; visually impaired;
hearing impaired; National Foundation
for Teaching Entrepreneurship to
Disadvantaged and Handicapped Youth

Typical grant range: $20,000 to $100,000

607

Ethel Sergeant Clark Smith Memorial Fund
First Union National Bank
123 S. Broad Street
Philadelphia, PA 19109
(215) 985-3920

Recording for the Blind; Cerebral Palsy
Association; Delco Blind/Sight Center;
Deaf-Hearing Communication Centre;
The Easter Seal Society; Society of the
Holy Child Jesus (accessibility project)

Grants awarded to organizations located
in Delaware County.

Typical grant range: $5,000 to $30,000

608

W.W. Smith Charitable Trust
3515 W. Chester Pike, Suite E
Newton Square, PA 19073-3705
(610) 359-1811

Physically and mentally disabled;
St. Edmonds Home for Crippled Children

Typical grant range: $10,000 to $50,000

609

Staunton Farm Foundation
Centre City Tower, Suite 210
650 Smithfield Street
Pittsburgh, PA 15222
(412) 281-8020

Pittsburgh Pastoral Institute (mental health
prevention, education and treatment); Try
Again Homes, Inc. (mental health
services); I Have A Dream Foundation
(mental health services); UPMC Western
Psychiatric Institute & Clinic (mental
health services)

Grants awarded to organizations located
in southwestern Pennsylvania.

Typical grant range: $5,000 to $40,000

610

Edith L. Trees Charitable Trust
c/o PNC Bank
One PNC Plaza, 2nd Floor
Pittsburgh, PA 15222
(412) 762-3803

Mentally and physically disabled; visually
impaired; youth; education; accessibility
project; Association for Retarded Citizens

Grants awarded to organizations located
in Pennsylvania.

Typical grant range: $10,000 to $75,000

611

Harry C. Trexler Trust
33 S. Seventh Street, Suite 205
Allentown, PA 18101
(610) 434-9645

Mentally and physically disabled;
Association for Retarded Citizens

Grants awarded to organizations located
in Lehigh County.

Typical grant range: $5,000 to $55,000

612

USX Foundation, Inc.
600 Grant Street, Room 685
Pittsburgh, PA 15219
(412) 433-5237

United Cerebral Palsy Association;
Recording for the Blind & Dyslexic;
Controlled Environment Horticulture
(employment program for people who
are disabled)

Grants awarded to organizations located
in areas of company operations (USX
Corporation).

Typical grant range: $3,000 to $45,000

613

**Widener Memorial Foundation in Aid
of Handicapped Children**
665 Thomas Road
P.O. Box 178
Lafayette Hill, PA 19444
(215) 836-7500

Physically disabled; youth; education;
accessibility projects; Episcopal Academy
(accessibility project)

Typical grant range: $7,500 to $75,000

614

Williamsport-Lycoming Foundation
220 West 4th Street, Suite C, 3rd Floor
Williamsport, PA 17701
(570) 321-1500

Special Olympics; Center for Independent
Living; Together Accessing Parks
(accessible playground for children with
special needs)

Grants awarded to organizations located
in Lycoming County.

PUERTO RICO

615

Puerto Rico Community Foundation
P.O. Box 70362
San Juan, PR 00936
(787) 721-1037

Physically disabled; Association of
Handicapped Persons

Grants awarded to organizations located
in Puerto Rico.

RHODE ISLAND

616

The Champlin Foundations
300 Centerville Road, Suite 300S
Warwick, RI 02886
(401) 736-0370

Mentally disabled; Association for
Retarded Citizens

Grants awarded to organizations located
in Rhode Island.

Typical grant range: $10,000 to $100,000

617

The North Family Trust
201 Waterman Avenue
East Providence, RI 02914

Physically disabled; Sail Newport (sailing
project for people who are disabled)

Most grants awarded to organizations
located in Newport County.

Typical grant range: $2,000 to $5,000

618

The Rhode Island Foundation
One Union Station
Providence, RI 02903
(401) 274-4564

East Bay Mental Health Center; South
Shore Mental Health Center (youth
program); St. Andrew's School (technology
program for students who are learning
disabled)

Grants awarded to organizations located
in Rhode Island.

Typical grant range: $2,500 to $75,000

SOUTH CAROLINA

619
Central Carolina Community Foundation
P.O. Box 11222
Columbia, SC 29211
(803) 254-5601

Sumter County Disabilities Board (computer learning center to train people who are developmentally disabled)

Typical grant range: $1,000 to $7,500

620
Hilton Head Island Foundation, Inc.
4 Northridge Drive, Suite A
P.O. Box 23019
Hilton Head Island, SC 29925
(803) 681-9100

Special Olympics of South Carolina (program for additional sports and volunteer training); Programs for Exceptional People (employment training programs for people who are disabled); Access Disability Action Center (counseling program for people who are physically disabled)

Grants awarded to organizations located in Hilton Head Island.

Typical grant range: $1,500 to $50,000

621
The Joanna Foundation
P.O. Box 308
Sullivan's Island, SC 29482
(843) 883-9199

Association for the Blind; Charleston Area Therapeutic Riding

Grants awarded in the following counties: Berkeley, Charleston, Dorchester, Laurens and Newberry.

Typical grant range: $1,000 to $10,000

622
The Self Family Foundation
P.O. Drawer 1017
Greenwood, SC 29648
(864) 941-4036

Mentally disabled; visually impaired; Orton Dyslexia Society; Episcopal Church Home for Children (services for families with children who are emotionally disturbed)

Grants awarded to organizations located in South Carolina, with an emphasis in the Greenwood vicinity.

Typical grant range: $5,000 to $75,000

623
John I. Smith Charities, Inc.
c/o Bank of America, Trust Dept.
P.O. Box 608
Greenville, SC 29608
(864) 271-5847

Physically disabled; mental health; Foundation for Multihandicapped

Grants awarded to organizations located in South Carolina.

Typical grant range: $1,000 to $50,000

SOUTH DAKOTA

624
Larson Foundation
2333 Eastbrook Drive
Brookings, SD 57006
(605) 692-6115

Physically disabled; Prairie Center for Disabled Independence

Grants awarded to organizations located in South Dakota.

Typical grant range: $500 to $15,000

625

South Dakota Community Foundation
207 East Capitol
P.O. Box 296
Pierre, SD 57501
(605) 224-1025

Physically disabled; developmentally
disabled; hearing impaired

Grants awarded to organizations located
in South Dakota.

Typical grant range: $300 to $11,000

TENNESSEE

626

The Assisi Foundation of Memphis, Inc.
6077 Primacy Parkway, Suite 253
Memphis, TN 38119

Hearing impaired; physically disabled;
Memphis Oral School for the Deaf

Grants awarded to organizations located
in the Memphis vicinity.

Typical grant range: $10,000 to $50,000

627

**Community Foundation of Greater
Memphis**
1900 Union Avenue
Memphis, TN 38104-4029
(901) 728-4600

Physically disabled; Center for
Independent Living (Zoo Day for people
with disabilities); People First of Tennessee,
Inc. (program for people with disabilities
who are moving out of state institutions)

628

**The Cracker Barrel Old Country Store
Foundation**
305 Hartmann Drive
Lebanon, TN 37087

Easter Seal Society of Nashville; Prevent
Blindness Tennessee; The Mental Health
Association in Nashville; Cumberland
Mental Health Services, Inc.

Most grants awarded to organizations
located in Tennessee.

Typical grant range: $500 to $10,000

629

The Frist Foundation
3319 W. End Avenue, Suite 900
Nashville, TN 37203
(615) 292-3868

Hearing impaired; mentally and
physically disabled; mental health;
accessibility project; League for the
Hearing Impaired

Most grants awarded to organizations
located in Nashville.

Typical grant range: $2,000 to $30,000

630

Lyndhurst Foundation
517 E. 5th Street
Chattanooga, TN 37403
(423) 756-0767

Southern Community Partners (health
care program for children who are
disabled)

Most grants awarded to organizations
located in Chattanooga.

Typical grant range: $25,000 to $120,000

631

Plough Foundation
6410 Poplar Avenue, Suite 710
Memphis, TN 38119-4863
(901) 761-9180

Arts for the Blind and Visually Impaired

Grants awarded to organizations located
in Memphis and in Shelby County.

Typical grant range: $10,000 to $200,000

632

The Thompson Charitable Foundation
P.O. Box 10516
Knoxville, TN 37939
(423) 588-0491

Hearing impaired; physically disabled;
Tennessee School for the Deaf

Typical grant range: $25,000 to $75,000

633
Robert Lee Weiss Foundation
c/o First Tennessee Bank, N.A.
Trust Division
800 South Gay Street
Knoxville, TN 37929
(423) 971-2165

Physically disabled; Goodwill Industries

TEXAS

634
Abell-Hanger Foundation
P.O. Box 430
Midland, TX 79702
(915) 684-6655

Texas Society to Prevent Blindness;
Midland Association for Retarded
Citizens; Cerebral Palsy Treatment
Center; National Multiple Sclerosis;
Rehabilitation Center for Children and
Adults; Recording Library for the Blind &
Physically Handicapped, Inc.; County
Council for Retarded Children, Inc.;
Opportunity Workshop (employment
program for people who are disabled);
Bynum School (program for students who
are developmentally disabled or learning
disabled)

Grants awarded to organizations located
in Texas.

Typical grant range: $5,000 to $70,000

635
The Brown Foundation, Inc.
P.O. Box 130646
Houston, TX 77219
(713) 523-6867

Visually impaired; mentally disabled;
Taping for the Blind

Grants awarded to organizations located
in Texas, with an emphasis in Houston.

Typical grant range: $7,500 to $100,000

636
The Burnett Foundation
801 Cherry Street, Suite 1400
Ft. Worth, TX 76102
(817) 877-3344

Goodwill Industries; Easter Seal Society
(hydrotherapy treatment program)

Most grants awarded to organizations
located in the Ft. Worth vicinity.

Typical grant range: $5,000 to $100,000

637
**The Gordon and Mary Cain
Foundation**
Eight Greenway Plaza, Suite 702
Houston, TX 77046
(713) 960-9283

Mentally and physically disabled; Retina
Research Foundation

Grants awarded to organizations located
in Houston.

Typical grant range: $1,000 to $10,000

638
Amon G. Carter Foundation
P.O. Box 1036
Ft. Worth, TX 76101
(817) 332-2783

Physically disabled; mental health;
visually impaired; Easter Seal Society;
Association for the Blind

Most grants awarded to organizations
located in Ft. Worth and Tarrant County.

Typical grant range: $2,000 to $75,000

639
The Cockrell Foundation
1600 Smith, Suite 3900
Houston, TX 77002
(713) 209-7500

Goodwill Industries; Taping for the Blind

Grants awarded to organizations located
in the Houston vicinity.

Typical grant range: $1,500 to $40,000

640
Community Foundation of Abilene
500 Chestnut, Suite 1509
P.O. Box 1001
Abilene, TX 79604
(915) 676-3883

Kenley School (grant to help children with learning disabilities); Mental Health Association (grant for the Resource Library)

Grants awarded to organizations located in the Abilene vicinity.

Typical grant range: $1,000 to $12,000

641
Dave Coy Foundation
c/o Bank of America
P.O. Box 121
San Antonio, TX 78291
(210) 270-5371

Visually impaired; developmentally disabled; Easter Seal Society; San Antonio Lighthouse for the Blind

Most grants awarded to organizations located in the San Antonio vicinity.

Typical grant range: $5,000 to $25,000

642
Nathalie and Gladys Dalkowitz Charitable Trust
c/o Bank of America
P.O. Box 121
San Antonio, TX 78291
(210) 270-5371

Sunshine Cottage for the Deaf (school for children who are deaf)

Grants awarded to organizations located in the San Antonio vicinity.

Typical grant range: $5,000 to $15,000

643
Katrine Menzing Deakins Charitable Trust
c/o Bank of America
P.O. Box 1317
Ft. Worth, TX 76101
(817) 390-6714

Prevent Blindness; Mental Health Association; Easter Seal Society

Grants awarded to organizations located in Texas, with an emphasis in the Ft. Worth vicinity.

Typical grant range: $1,000 to $30,000

644
Dodge Jones Foundation
P.O. Box 176
Abilene, TX 79604
(915) 673-6429

Mentally and physically disabled; Disability Resources

Grants awarded to organizations located in Abilene.

Typical grant range: $1,000 to $50,000

645
John S. Dunn Research Foundation
3355 W. Alabama, Suite 720
Houston, TX 77098
(713) 626-0368

Mental health; physically disabled; visually impaired; hearing impaired; Texas Mental Health Association; Shriners Hospital for Crippled Children

Grants awarded to organizations located in Texas.

Typical grant range: $25,000 to $250,000

646
El Paso Community Foundation
201 East Main, Suite 1616
El Paso, TX 79901
(915) 533-4020

Mentally and physically disabled;
Christmas in April (home repair program
for low income, disabled and elderly); El
Paso Employment Services (employment
program for people who are disabled or
elderly)

Grants awarded to organizations located
in the El Paso vicinity.

647
Exxon Education Foundation
5959 Las Colinas Blvd.
Irving, TX 75039
(972) 444-1104

Special Olympics; National Multiple
Sclerosis Society; Mental Health
Association; National Organization on
Disability; Easter Seal Society for
Children

Typical grant range: $3,000 to $50,000

648
Leland Fikes Foundation, Inc.
3050 Lincoln Plaza
500 N. Akard
Dallas, TX 75201
(214) 754-0144

Physically and mentally disabled;
United Cerebral Palsy

Grants awarded to organizations located
in Dallas.

Typical grant range: $3,000 to $50,000

649
The Fleming Foundation
500 W. Seventh Street, Suite 1007
Ft. Worth, TX 76102

Physically disabled; Easter Seal Society

Most grants awarded to organizations
located in the Ft. Worth vicinity.

Typical grant range: $500 to $25,000

650
The George Foundation
304 Morton Street, Suite C
Richmond, TX 77469
(281) 342-6109

Physically disabled; speech impaired;
visually impaired; youth; accessibility
project

Most grants awarded to organizations
located in Ft. Bend County.

Typical grant range: $5,000 to $40,000

651
Hahl Proctor Charitable Trust
c/o Bank of America
P.O. Box 270
Midland, TX 79702
(915) 685-2103

Recording Library for the Blind; National
Multiple Sclerosis Society

Grants awarded to organizations located
in Midland.

Typical grant range: $2,000 to $12,000

652
The Ewing Halsell Foundation
711 Navarro Street, Suite 537
San Antonio, TX 78205
(210) 223-2640

Physically disabled; recreation; San
Antonio Area Rehabilitation Association

Most grants awarded to organizations
located in San Antonio.

Typical grant range: $1,000 to $35,000

653
Hillcrest Foundation
c/o Bank of America
Trust Division
P.O. Box 830241
Dallas, TX 75283
(214) 508-1965

Mentally and physically disabled; youth;
Texas Scottish Rite Hospital for Crippled
Children

Grants awarded to organizations located
in Texas, with an emphasis in Dallas.

Typical grant range: $5,000 to $50,000

654

Hoblitzelle Foundation
5956 Sherry Lane, Suite 901
Dallas, TX 75225
(214) 373-0462

Physically and mentally disabled; visually impaired; hearing impaired; autism; Center for Computer Assistance to the Disabled (equipment to help train people who are visually impaired); Camp John Marc/Special Camps for Special Kids (cabin for children who are disabled and chronically ill)

Grants awarded to organizations located in Texas, with an emphasis in Dallas.

Typical grant range: $15,000 to $75,000

655

Houston Endowment, Inc.
600 Travis, Suite 6400
Houston, TX 77002
(713) 238-8100

Goodwill Industries; Taping for the Blind, Inc.; Recording for the Blind & Dyslexic, Inc.; Gulf Coast Alliance for the Mentally Ill; The Center for Hearing and Speech; Houston Ear Research Foundation; Mental Health Association of Houston (education and training program); Bay Area Rehabilitation Center (program for people who are disabled); Methodist Mission Home (vocational rehabilitative program for people who are hearing impaired)

Grants awarded to organizations located in Houston.

Typical grant range: $10,000 to $250,000

656

Harris and Eliza Kempner Fund
P.O. Box 119
Galveston, TX 77553
(409) 762-1603

Mentally and physically disabled; visually impaired; Center for the Blind

Most grants awarded to organizations located in the Galveston vicinity.

Typical grant range: $1,000 to $15,000

657

Robert J. Kleberg, Jr. and Helen C. Kleberg Foundation
700 N. St. Mary's Street, Suite 1200
San Antonio, TX 78205
(210) 271-3691

Physically disabled; hearing impaired; eye research; Goodwill Industries

Most grants awarded to organizations located in Texas.

Typical grant range: $5,000 to $40,000

658

Robert W. Knox, Sr. and Pearl Wallis Knox Charitable Foundation
c/o Bank of America
P.O. Box 2518
Houston, TX 77252-2518
(713) 247-6000

Mental health; mentally and physically disabled; Goodwill Industries; Texas Special Olympics; Mental Health Association

Grants awarded to organizations located in Houston.

Typical grant range: $500 to $10,000

659

Marcia and Otto Koehler Foundation
c/o Bank of America
Private Clients Group
P.O. Box 121
San Antonio, TX 78291
(210) 270-5314

Southwest Guide Dogs; Sunshine Cottage for the Deaf (school for children who are deaf)

Grants awarded to organizations located in the San Antonio vicinity.

Typical grant range: $5,000 to $25,000

660
Helen Irwin Littauer Educational Trust
c/o Bank of America
P.O. Box 1317
Ft. Worth, TX 76101
(817) 390-6921

Physically disabled; visually impaired; mental health; Easter Seal Society; Mental Health Housing Development

Grants awarded to organizations located in Texas.

Typical grant range: $1,000 to $10,000

661
Robert E. and Evelyn McKee Foundation
P.O. Box 220599
6006 N. Mesa Street, Suite 906
El Paso, TX 79913
(915) 581-4025

Texas Special Olympics; Therapeutic Horsemanship; International Hearing Dog, Inc.

Most grants awarded to organizations located in Texas, with an emphasis in El Paso.

Typical grant range: $500 to $7,500

662
Meadows Foundation, Inc.
Wilson Historic Block
3003 Swiss Avenue
Dallas, TX 75204
(214) 826-9431

Gulf Coast Alliance for the Mentally Ill; Recording for the Blind & Dyslexic; Easter Seal Society for Children; Texas Department of Mental Health and Mental Retardation; Center for Crippled Children and Adults; Notre Dame of Dallas Schools (school serving children who are developmentally disabled); University of Texas (technology center for hearing research); Equest (therapeutic riding center for people who are disabled); Family Counseling Service (mental health services for the elderly); Mental Health Association (program targeting teenagers); Goodwill Industries (equipment for a job training program); Bay Area Rehabilitation Center (program for people who are physically disabled)

Grants awarded to organizations located in Texas.

Typical grant range: $10,000 to $200,000

663
Paul J. Meyer Family Foundation
P.O. Box 7411
Waco, TX 76714

Physically disabled; Special Needs Ministries

Most grants awarded to organizations located in Waco.

664
The Moody Foundation
2302 Postoffice Street, Suite 704
Galveston, TX 77550
(409) 763-5333

Learning disabled; physically disabled; Children's Hospital (building funds for an accessible playground); Moody Scholars Program (program for high school seniors who are learning disabled); Dallas Academy (program for students who are learning disabled)

Grants awarded to organizations located in Texas.

Typical grant range: $15,000 to $250,000

665
Carrie S. Orleans Trust
c/o Bank of America
P.O. Box 831041
Dallas, TX 75283
(214) 559-6321

Visually impaired; Dallas Lighthouse for the Blind

Grants awarded to organizations located in Dallas.

Typical grant range: $1,000 to $7,000

666
RGK Foundation
1301 W. 25th Street, Suite 300
Austin, TX 78705
(512) 474-9298

Visually impaired; mentally and physically disabled; Texas Society to Prevent Blindness (vision screening program); Down Home Ranch (employment program for people who are mentally disabled); Challenge Air for Kids & Friends (motivational and recreational program for children who are disabled or disadvantaged)

Typical grant range: $3,000 to $50,000

667
Sid W. Richardson Foundation
309 Main Street
Ft. Worth, TX 76102
(817) 336-0494

Mentally and physically disabled; visually impaired; mental health; Taping for the Blind; Texas Society to Prevent Blindness; Opportunity Workshop, Inc. (program for people who are mentally and physically disabled)

Grants awarded to organizations located in Texas.

Typical grant range: $10,000 to $125,000

668
Rockwell Fund, Inc.
1360 Post Oak Blvd., Suite 780
Houston, TX 77056
(713) 629-9022

Mental Health Association of Houston; Mental Health and Mental Retardation Authority; The Center for Hearing and Speech; The Dyslexia Foundation; Foundation for the Retarded; Hermann Eye Fund; Houston Eye Associates; Foundation Taping for the Blind, Inc.

Grants awarded to organizations located in Texas, with an emphasis in Houston.

Typical grant range: $5,000 to $25,000

669
W. L. & Louise E. Seymour Foundation
Chase Bank
P.O. Drawer 140
El Paso, TX 79980
(915) 546-6515

Physically disabled; youth; education

Grants awarded to organizations located in El Paso.

Typical grant range: $2,000 to $20,000

670
Bob and Vivian Smith Foundation
1900 W. Loop South, Suite 1050
Houston, TX 77027
(713) 622-8611

The Richmond State School (therapeutic riding center)

Most grants awarded to organizations located in Houston.

671
The Stein Family Charitable Trust
c/o Bank of America
P.O. Box 1317
Ft. Worth, TX 76101
(817) 390-6916

Hearing impaired; emotionally disturbed; physically disabled; youth; cultural program; Imagination Celebration (artistic program for students who are hearing impaired)

Grants awarded to organizations located in Tarrant County.

Typical grant range: $2,500 to $5,000

672
Strake Foundation
712 Main Street, Suite 3300
Houston, TX 77002
(713) 216-2400

Mentally disabled; Goodwill Industries

Grants awarded to organizations located in Texas, with an emphasis in Houston.

Typical grant range: $2,500 to $20,000

673
Roy and Christine Sturgis Charitable and Educational Trust
c/o Bank of America
P.O. Box 830241
Dallas, TX 75283
(214) 508-1965

Visually impaired; physically disabled; Lighthouse for the Blind

Typical grant range: $10,000 to $75,000

674
Swalm Foundation
11511 Katy Freeway, Suite 430
Houston, TX 77079
(281) 497-5280

Hearing impaired; visually impaired; mental health

Grants awarded to organizations located in Texas.

675
T.L.L. Temple Foundation
109 Temple Blvd., Suite 300
Lufkin, TX 75901
(409) 639-5197

Mentally and physically disabled; youth; education; Special Olympics

Grants awarded to organizations located in the Deep East Texas Pine Timber Belt.

Typical grant range: $10,000 to $150,000

676
The Trull Foundation
404 Fourth Street
Palacios, TX 77465
(512) 972-5241

Visually impaired; Recording for the Blind and Dyslexic; Christian Education for the Blind, Inc.

Typical grant range: $500 to $12,000

677
Rachael & Ben Vaughan Foundation
P.O. Box 2233
Austin, TX 78768
(512) 477-4726

Hearing impaired; Recording for the Blind and Dyslexic; Karen E. Henry Foundation for Long Term Housing for Persons with Disabilities; Goodwill Industries (accessibility project); Austin Child Guidance Center (mental health services); Down Home Ranch (program for people who are mentally disabled)

Typical grant range: $500 to $8,000

678
The Waco Foundation
900 Austin Avenue, Suite 1000
Waco, TX 76701
(254) 754-3404

Mentally disabled; Association for
Retarded Citizens

Grants awarded to organizations located
in the Waco vicinity.

Typical grant range: $2,000 to $30,000

679
Crystelle Waggoner Charitable Trust
P.O. Box 1317
Ft. Worth, TX 76101
(817) 390-6114

Mental health; physically disabled; youth;
Mental Health Housing Development
Corp.

Typical grant range: $1,000 to $15,000

UTAH

680
The Ashton Family Foundation
251 River Park Drive, Suite 350
Provo, UT 84604
(801) 226-1266

Visually impaired; hearing impaired;
Prevent Blindness

Most grants awarded to organizations
located in Utah.

Typical grant range: $1,000 to $10,000

681
**Dr. Ezekiel R. and Edna Wattis Dumke
Foundation**
P.O. Box 776
Kaysville, UT 84037
(801) 497-9474

United Cerebral Palsy; Easter Seals of
Utah; Utah Down Syndrome Foundation;
Recreation and Habilitation Services
(education, recreation and therapeutic
activities program for children who are
mentally disabled); National Society
to Prevent Blindness (free screening
program for glaucoma); Mental Health
Association (education and screening
program)

Typical grant range: $2,000 to $15,000

682
**The George S. and Dolores Dore Eccles
Foundation**
Deseret Building, 12th Floor
79 S. Main Street
Salt Lake City, UT 84111
(801) 246-5336

Physically disabled; visually impaired;
Utah Assistive Technology Foundation
(equipment for people who are disabled)

Most grants awarded to organizations
located in Utah.

Typical grant range: $3,000 to $75,000

683
**Willard L. Eccles Charitable
Foundation**
P.O. Box 45385
Salt Lake City, UT 84145
(801) 532-1500

Visually impaired; mental health; Prevent
Blindness

Grants awarded to organizations located
in Utah.

Typical grant range: $5,000 to $45,000

684
Dr. W. C. Swanson Family Foundation
2955 Harrison Blvd., Suite 201
Ogden, UT 84403
(801) 392-0360

Mentally and physically disabled; visually
impaired; Special Olympics

Grants awarded to organizations located
in Utah, with an emphasis in Weber
County.

Typical grant range: $1,500 to $50,000

VERMONT

685
Lintilhac Foundation
100 Harbor Road
Shelburne, VT 05482
(802) 985-4106

Visually impaired; hearing impaired;
Vermont Association for the Blind

Typical grant range: $500 to $15,000

686
The Vermont Community Foundation
P.O. Box 30
Middlebury, VT 05753
(802) 388-3355

Physically disabled; mental health

Grants awarded to organizations located
in Vermont.

VIRGINIA

687
Beazley Foundation, Inc.
3720 Brighton Street
Portsmouth, VA 23707
(757) 393-1605

Physically disabled; visually impaired;
Special Olympics

Most grants awarded to organizations
located in the South Hampton Roads
vicinity.

Typical grant range: $5,000 to $75,000

688
Inez Duff Bishop Charitable Trust
Central Fidelity Bank
P.O. Box 27602
Richmond, VA 23261

Visually impaired; Recording for the
Blind and Dyslexic

Most grants awarded to organizations
located in Charlottesville, Virginia.

Typical grant range: $500 to $6,000

689
**The Community Foundation Serving
Richmond & Central Virginia**
7325 Beaufont Springs Drive, Suite 210
Richmond, VA 23225
(804) 330-7400

Special Olympics; Virginia Voice for the
Print Handicapped, Inc.; Christmas in
April (home repair program for low
income, disabled and elderly)

Grants awarded to organizations located
in the Richmond vicinity and central
Virginia.

Typical grant range: $1,000 to $20,000

690
The Memorial Foundation for Children
P.O. Box 8342
Richmond, VA 23226

Mentally and physically disabled;
Association for Retarded Citizens

Grants awarded to organizations helping
children.

Grants awarded to organizations located
in the Richmond vicinity.

691

The Norfolk Foundation
One Commercial Place, Suite 1410
Norfolk, VA 23510
(757) 622-7951

United Cerebral Palsy (office equipment);
Accessible Housing Corp. (provide
assistance devices for residents with
disabilities); Child Abuse Prevention
Services of the St. Mary's Home for
Disabled Children (office equipment)

Grants awarded to organizations located
in the Norfolk vicinity.

Typical grant range: $10,000 to $75,000

692

Norfolk Southern Foundation
P.O. Box 3040
Norfolk, VA 23514
(757) 629-2640

Mental health; visually impaired; Mental
Health Association

Typical grant range: $1,000 to $30,000

693

**Northern Virginia Community
Foundation**
8283 Greensboro Drive
McLean, VA 22102
(703) 917-2600

Head Injuries Partnership; Social Center
for Psychiatric Rehabilitation; Loudoun
4-H Therapeutic Riding; United Cerebral
Palsy of Washington and Northern Virginia

Grants awarded to organizations located
in northern Virginia.

Typical grant range: $500 to $5,000

694

Portsmouth Community Trust
P.O. Box 1394
Portsmouth, VA 23705
(757) 397-5424

United Cerebral Palsy; Virginia Special
Olympics

Grants awarded to organizations located
in the Portsmouth vicinity.

Typical grant range: $1,000 to $15,000

695

Richard S. Reynolds Foundation
1403 Pemberton Road, Suite 102
Richmond, VA 23233
(804) 740-7350

Physically disabled; dyslexia; Multiple
Sclerosis Society

Most grants awarded to organizations
located in Virginia.

Typical grant range: $2,000 to $50,000

696

**C.E. Richardson Benevolent
Foundation**
202 N. Washington Avenue
Pulaski, VA 24301
(540) 980-6628

Mental Health Association; Easter Seal
Society; Virginia Special Olympics;
National Multiple Sclerosis Society; New
River Valley Agency for the Mentally
Retarded

Typical grant range: $1,000 to $10,000

697

The Virginia Beach Foundation
P.O. Box 4629
Virginia Beach, VA 23454
(757) 422-5249

Equi-Kids (therapeutic riding program);
The Easter Seal Society (therapeutic
recreation program and respite care
services); Children's Hospital of the
King's Daughters (speech language
department); United Cerebral Palsy
(temporary relief for parents of a child or
adult who is developmentally disabled)

Grants awarded to organizations located
in the Virginia Beach vicinity.

698

Washington Forrest Foundation
2300 S. Ninth Street
Arlington, VA 22204
(703) 920-3688

Easter Seal Society; Bilingual Mental
Health Support; Alternative House
(Depression Intervention Program)

Typical grant range: $500 to $8,000

WASHINGTON

699
The Paul G. Allen Charitable Foundation
1111 Third Avenue Building, Suite 2400
Seattle, WA 98101

Visually impaired; hearing impaired; physically disabled; Special Olympics

Typical grant range: $10,000 to $100,000

700
Ben B. Cheney Foundation, Inc.
1201 Pacific Avenue, Suite 1600
Tacoma, WA 98402
(253) 572-2442

Physically and mentally disabled; youth; cultural organizations; accessibility project; Special Olympics

Typical grant range: $2,000 to $50,000

701
Florence B. Kilworth Charitable Foundation
c/o KeyTrust Company
P.O. Box 11500, MS: WA31-01-0310
Tacoma, WA 98411-5052
(253) 305-7206

Northwest Center for Hearing-Impaired Children

Grants awarded to organizations located in Tacoma and in Pierce County.

Typical grant range: $1,000 to $10,000

702
Elizabeth A. Lynn Foundation
PMB 6159
13300 Bothell Everett Highway
Mill Creek, WA 98012
(425) 316-6842

Hearing impaired; physically disabled; Northwest School for Hearing Impaired Children

Grants awarded to organizations located in Washington, with an emphasis on the Puget Sound vicinity.

Typical grant range: $1,000 to $20,000

703
Medina Foundation
1300 Norton Building
801 Second Avenue, 13th Floor
Seattle, WA 98104
(206) 464-5231

Mental health; physically disabled; Community Psychiatric Clinic

Grants awarded to organizations located in the Puget Sound vicinity.

Typical grant range: $2,000 to $25,000

704
M.J. Murdock Charitable Trust
P.O. Box 1618
Vancouver, WA 98668
(360) 694-8415

Special Olympics; Easter Seal Society; Bridge Ministries for Disability Concerns; Northwest School for Hearing Impaired Children

Typical grant range: $20,000 to $250,000

705
The Norcliffe Foundation
999 Third Avenue, Suite 1006
Seattle, WA 98104
(206) 682-4820

Physically disabled; visually impaired; Easter Seal Society

Grants awarded to organizations located in the Puget Sound vicinity.

Typical grant range: $1,000 to $25,000

WEST VIRGINIA

706
Beckley Area Foundation, Inc.
P.O. Box 1092
Beckley, WV 25802
(304) 253-3806

Special Olympics (uniforms and equipment); Quota International (scholarships for people who are hearing impaired)

Grants awarded to organizations located in the Beckley vicinity.

707

Clay Foundation, Inc.
1426 Kanawha Blvd., East
Charleston, WV 25301
(304) 344-8656

Physically disabled; Goodwill Industries

Grants awarded to organizations located
in West Virginia, with an emphasis in the
greater Kanawha Valley vicinity.

Typical grant range: $5,000 to $60,000

708

**The Greater Kanawha Valley
Foundation**
P.O. Box 3041
Charleston, WV 25331-3041
(304) 346-3620

West Virginia Special Olympics;
Association for Retarded Citizens;
National Multiple Sclerosis Society;
South Central WV Chapter of the Autism
Society of America, Inc.; Mental Health
Association in the Greater Kanawha
Valley (Internet service); East Bank High
School (transportation for students who
are mentally disabled to interact in
community settings)

Grants awarded to organizations located
in the Greater Kanawha Valley.

Typical grant range: $1,000 to $7,000

709

Bernard McDonough Foundation, Inc.
311 4th Street
Parkersburg, WV 26101-5315
(304) 424-6280

Physically disabled; Special Olympics;
Disabled American Veterans

Most grants awarded to organizations
located in West Virginia.

710

**Parkersburg Area Community
Foundation**
P.O. Box 1762
Parkersburg, WV 26102
(304) 428-4438

Mentally and physically disabled; The ARC

Grants awarded to organizations located
in the Parkersburg vicinity.

WISCONSIN

711

Judd S. Alexander Foundation, Inc.
500 Third Street, Suite 320
P.O. Box 2137
Wausau, WI 54402
(715) 845-4556

Visually impaired; United Cerebral Palsy

Grants awarded to organizations located
in Marathon County.

Typical grant range: $2,000 to $30,000

712

Helen Bader Foundation, Inc.
233 N. Water Street
Milwaukee, WI 53202
(414) 224-6464

Lutheran Social Services (accessibility
project); United Community Center, Inc.
(accessible elevator at an adult day
center); National Spinal Cord Injury
Association (building funds at the State
Fair Park for visitors with disabilities)

Most grants awarded to organizations
located in the Milwaukee vicinity.

Typical grant range: $2,000 to $100,000

713

**The Lynde and Harry Bradley
Foundation, Inc.**
P.O. Box 510860
Milwaukee, WI 53203
(414) 291-9915

Prevent Blindness; Volunteer Services for
the Visually Handicapped

Typical grant range: $20,000 to $120,000

714
Patrick and Anna M. Cudahy Fund
P.O. Box 11978
Milwaukee, WI 53211
(847) 866-0760

Recording for the Blind & Dyslexic;
Housing Options for the Mentally Ill;
Center for Deaf-Blind Persons; Easter
Seal Society; The Hadley School for the
Blind; United Cerebral Palsy; National
Lekotek Center (services for children with
disabilities); Fishing Has No Boundaries
(Anglers with Disabilities)

Typical grant range: $2,000 to $25,000

715
**Elizabeth Elser Doolittle Charitable
Trust No. 1**
c/o Foley & Lardner
777 E. Wisconsin Avenue
Milwaukee, WI 53202
(414) 297-5734

Mentally and physically disabled; visually
impaired; youth

Most grants awarded to organizations
located in Wisconsin.

Typical grant range: $1,000 to $7,500

716
Madison Community Foundation
615 E. Washington Avenue
P.O. Box 71
Madison, WI 53701
(608) 255-0503

Very Special Arts Wisconsin (classes for
adults who are disabled)

Grants awarded to organizations located
in the Madison vicinity.

Typical grant range: $1,000 to $35,000

717
Faye McBeath Foundation
1020 North Broadway
Milwaukee, WI 53202
(414) 272-2626

Physically disabled; visually impaired;
youth; cultural programs

Grants awarded to organizations located in
Wisconsin, with an emphasis in Milwaukee.

718
**Northwestern Mutual Life
Foundation, Inc.**
720 E. Wisconsin Avenue
Milwaukee, WI 53202
(414) 299-2200

Visually impaired; mentally disabled;
Volunteer Services for the Visually
Handicapped

Most grants awarded to organizations
located in Milwaukee.

Typical grant range: $5,000 to $100,000

719
Jane B. Pettit Foundation, Inc.
660 E. Mason Street
Milwaukee, WI 53202
(414) 271-5900

Alliance for the Mentally Ill; Goodwill
Industries; Center for Blind and Visually
Impaired Children

Grants awarded to organizations located
in Milwaukee.

Typical grant range: $2,500 to $50,000

720
**The L.E. Phillips Family
Foundation, Inc.**
3925 N. Hastings Way
Eau Claire, WI 54703
(715) 839-2139

Easter Seal Society; Special Olympics;
Center for Independent Living; United
Cerebral Palsy; Courage Center (summer
camp for people who are disabled)

Typical grant range: $350 to $15,000

721
**The Oscar Rennebohm
Foundation, Inc.**
P.O. Box 5187
Madison, WI 53719
(608) 274-5991

Physically disabled; Very Special Arts

Grants awarded to organizations located
in Wisconsin.

722
Wisconsin Energy Corporation Foundation
231 W. Michigan Street
Milwaukee, WI 53201
(414) 221-2106

Special Olympics; United Cerebral Palsy; Alliance for the Mentally Ill; Association for the Developmentally Disabled; Association for the Developmentally Disabled; Autism Society of Southeastern Wisconsin; Wisconsin Dyslexia Institute; Center for Blind & Visually Impaired Children; Center for Deaf-Blind Persons; March of Dimes

Grants awarded to organizations located in areas of company operations.

Typical grant range: $1,000 to $35,000

723
Ziemann Foundation, Inc.
830 Armor Road, Suite 8
Oconomowoc, WI 53066
(262) 569-9330

Physically and mentally disabled; youth; Special Olympics

Grants awarded to organizations located in Wisconsin.

Typical grant range: $2,000 to $9,000

WYOMING

724
Community Foundation of Jackson Hole
P.O. Box 574
Jackson, WY 83001
(307) 739-1026

The Learning Center (education program for children with disabilities); Jackson Hole Therapeutic Riding Association (program for people who are physically disabled); Teton Science School (build a nature trail accessible to people with disabilities)

Grants awarded to organizations located in Teton County.

Typical grant range: $500 to $5,000

725
Mary & Doc Robertson Handicapped Children's Trust
c/o Norwest Bank Wyoming
234 E. 1st Street
Casper, WY 82602
(307) 235-7750

Mentally and physically disabled; emphasis on youth; prevention and treatment programs

Most grants awarded to organizations located in Casper.

726
Homer A. Scott and Mildred S. Scott Foundation
P.O. Box 2007
Sheridan, WY 82801
(307) 672-1404

Northern Wyoming Mental Health Center

Grants awarded to organizations located in Sheridan.

727
Wyoming Community Foundation
221 E. Ivinson Avenue, Suite 202
Laramie, WY 82070
(307) 721-8300

Wyoming Independent Living Rehabilitation, Inc.

Grants awarded to organizations located in Wyoming.

Appendix A
The Foundation Center

The Foundation Center is an independent national service organization established by foundations to provide an authoritative source of information on private philanthropic giving. The Center disseminates this information through public service programs, publications and through a national network of library reference collections for free public use. The New York, Washington, DC, Atlanta, Cleveland and San Francisco reference collections operated by the Foundation Center offer a wide variety of services and comprehensive information on foundations and grants. The Cooperating Collections are libraries, community foundations and other nonprofit agencies that provide a core collection of Foundation Center publications and a variety of supplementary materials and services in subject areas useful to grant seekers.

Many of the network members make available sets of private foundation information returns (IRS Form 990-PF) for their state and/or neighboring states. A complete set of U.S. foundation returns can be found at the New York and Washington, DC, offices of the Foundation Center. The Atlanta, Cleveland, and San Francisco offices contain IRS Form 990-PF returns for the southeastern, midwestern, and western states, respectively.

Those collections marked with a bullet (•) have sets of private foundation returns (IRS Form 990-PF) for their states or regions, available for public reference.

Because the collections vary in their hours, materials and services, IT IS RECOMMENDED THAT YOU CALL EACH COLLECTION IN ADVANCE.

To check on new locations or current information, call toll-free 1-800-424-9836.

Reference Collections
• The Foundation Center
79 Fifth Ave., 2nd Fl.
New York, NY 10003
(212) 620-4230
• The Foundation Center
312 Sutter St., Room 312
San Francisco, CA 94108
(415) 397-0902
• The Foundation Center
1001 Connecticut Ave., NW
Washington, DC 20036
(202) 331-1400
• The Foundation Center
Kent H. Smith Library
1422 Euclid, Suite 1356
Cleveland, OH 44115
(216) 861-1933
• The Foundation Center
Suite 150, Grand Lobby
Hurt Building, 50 Hurt Plaza
Atlanta, GA 30303
(404) 880-0094

COOPERATING COLLECTIONS
Alabama
• Birmingham Public Library
Government Documents
2100 Park Place
Birmingham, AL 35203
(205) 226-3600

Huntsville Public Library
915 Monroe Street
Huntsville, AL 35801
(256) 532-5940
• University of South Alabama
Library Building
Mobile, AL 36688
(334) 460-7025
• Auburn University at
Montgomery Library
7300 University Drive
Montgomery, AL 36117
(334) 244-3653
Alaska
• University of Alaska at
Anchorage Library
3211 Providence Drive
Anchorage, AK 99508
(907) 786-1847
Juneau Public Library
Reference
292 Marine Way
Juneau, AK 99801
(907) 586-5267
Arizona
• Phoenix Public Library
Information Services Dept.
1221 N. Central
Phoenix, AZ 85004
(602) 262-4636

• Tucson Pima Library
101 N. Stone Avenue
Tucson, AZ 87501
(520) 791-4010
Arkansas
• Westark Community College
Borham Library
5210 Grand Avenue
Fort Smith, AR 72913
(501) 788-7200
• Central Arkansas Library System
700 Louisiana
Little Rock, AR 72201
(501) 370-5952
Pine Bluff-Jefferson County
Library System
200 East Eighth
Pine Bluff, AR 71601
(870) 534-2159
California
• Humboldt Area Foundation
P.O. Box 99
Bayside, CA 95524
(707) 442-2993
• Ventura Co. Comm. Foundation
Resource Center for
Nonprofit Organizations
1317 Del Norte Road, Suite 150
Camarillo, CA 93010
(805) 988-0196

Fresno Regional Foundation
Nonprofit Advancement Center
1999 Tuolumne Street, Suite 650
Fresno, CA 93721
(209) 498-3929

Center for Nonprofit Management in
Southern California
314 West Ninth Street, Suite 1100
Los Angeles, CA 90015
(213) 623-7080

East Bay Resource Center for
Nonprofit Support
1203 Preservation Parkway, Suite 100
Oakland, CA 94612
(510) 834-1010

Flintridge Foundation
Philanthropy Resource Library
1040 Lincoln Avenue, Suite 100
Pasadena, CA 91103
(626) 449-0839

• Grant and Resource Center of
Northern California
Building C, Suite A
2280 Benton Drive
Redding, CA 96003
(916) 244-1219

Los Angeles Public Library
West Valley Regional Branch Library
19036 Van Owen Street
Reseda, CA 91335
(818) 345-4393

Riverside Public Library
3581 Mission Inn Avenue
Riverside, CA 92501
(919) 782-5202

Nonprofit Resource Center
Sacramento Public Library
828 I Street, 2nd Floor
Sacramento, CA 95814
(916) 264-2772

• San Diego Foundation
Funding Information Center
1420 Kettner Blvd., Suite 500
San Diego, CA 92101
(619) 239-8815

• The Foundation Center
312 Sutter Street, Room 312
San Francisco, CA 94108
(415) 397-0902

Nonprofit Development
Center Library
1922 The Alameda, Suite 212
San Jose, CA 95126
(408) 248-9505

• Peninsula Community Foundation
Peninsula Nonprofit Center
1700 S. El Camino Real, R201
San Mateo, CA 94402
(650) 358-9392

Los Angeles Public Library
San Pedro Regional Branch
9131 S. Gaffey Street
San Pedro, CA 90731
(310) 548-7779

Volunteer Center of Greater
Orange County
Nonprofit Management Assistance Ctr.
1901 E. Fourth Street, Suite 100
Santa Ana, CA 92705
(714) 953-5757

Santa Barbara Public Library
40 East Anapamu Street
Santa Barbara, CA 93101
(805) 962-7653

Santa Monica Public Library
1343 Sixth Street
Santa Monica, CA 90401
(310) 458-8600

Sonoma County Library
3rd & E Streets
Santa Rosa, CA 95404
(707) 545-0831

Seaside Branch Library
550 Harcourt Street
Seaside, CA 93955
(408) 899-8131

Sonora Area Foundation
20100 Cedar Road, N.
Sonora, CA 95370
(209) 533-2596

Colorado
El Pomar Nonprofit Resource Center
1661 Mesa Avenue
Colorado Springs, CO 80906
(800) 554-7711

• Denver Public Library
General Reference
10 West 14th Ave. Pkwy.
Denver, CO 80204
(303) 640-6200

Connecticut
Danbury Public Library
170 Main Street
Danbury, CT 06810
(203) 797-4527

• Greenwich Library
101 W. Putnam Avenue
Greenwich, CT 06830
(203) 622-7910

• Hartford Public Library
500 Main Street
Hartford, CT 06103
(860) 543-8656

New Haven Free Public Library
Reference Department
133 Elm Street
New Haven, CT 06510
(203) 946-8130

Delaware
• University of Delaware
Hugh Morris Library
Newark, DE 19717
(302) 831-2432

District of Columbia
• The Foundation Center
1001 Connecticut Avenue, NW
Washington, DC 20036
(202) 331-1400

Florida
Volusia County Library Center
City Island
Daytona Beach, FL 32014
(904) 257-6036

• Nova Southeastern University
Einstein Library
3301 College Avenue
Ft. Lauderdale, FL 33314
(954) 262-4601

Indian River Comm. College
Charles S. Miley Learning
Resource Center
3209 Virginia Avenue
Ft. Pierce, FL 34981
(561) 462-4757

• Jacksonville Public Libraries
Grants Resource Center
122 North Ocean Street
Jacksonville, FL 32202
(904) 630-2665

• Miami-Dade Public Library
Humanities/Social Science
101 W. Flagler Street
Miami, FL 33130
(305) 375-5575

• Orlando Public Library
Social Sciences Department
101 E. Central Blvd.
Orlando, FL 32801
(407) 425-4694

Selby Public Library-Reference
1331 1st Street
Sarasota, FL 34236
(941) 316-1181

• Tampa-Hillsborough County
Public Library
900 N. Ashley Drive
Tampa, FL 33602
(813) 273-3628
• Community Foundation for
Palm Beach and Martin Counties
324 Datura Street, Suite 340
West Palm Beach, FL 33401
(561) 659-6800

Georgia
• Atlanta-Fulton Public Library
Foundation Collection
Ivan Allen Department
1 Margaret Mitchell Square
Atlanta, GA 30303
(404) 730-1900
• The Foundation Center
Suite 150, Grand Lobby
Hurt Building, 50 Hurt Plaza
Atlanta, GA 30303
(404) 880-0094
• United Way of Georgia
Community Resource Center
277 Martin Luther King Jr. Blvd.
Suite 301
Macon, GA 31201
(912) 745-4732
Savannah State University
Asa Gordon Library
Savannah, GA 31404
(912) 356-2185
• Thomas County Public Library
201 N. Madison St.
Thomasville, GA 31792
(912) 225-5252

Hawaii
• University of Hawaii
Hamilton Library
2550 The Mall
Honolulu, HI 96822
(808) 956-7214
Hawaii Community Foundation
Resource Library
900 Fort Street, Suite 1300
Honolulu, HI 96813
(808) 537-6333

Idaho
• Boise Public Library
715 S. Capitol Blvd.
Boise, ID 83702
(208) 384-4024
• Caldwell Public Library
1010 Dearborn Street
Caldwell, ID 83605
(208) 459-3242

Illinois
• Donors Forum of Chicago
208 S. LaSalle Street, Suite 735
Chicago, IL 60604
(312) 578-0175
• Evanston Public Library
1703 Orrington Avenue
Evanston, IL 60201
(847) 866-0305
Rock Island Public Library
401 - 19th Street
Rock Island, IL 61201
(309) 788-7627
• University of Illinois at Springfield
Brookens Library
Shepherd Road
Springfield, IL 62794
(217) 206-6633

Indiana
Evansville-Vanderburgh County
Public Library
22 Southeast Fifth Street
Evansville, IN 47708
(812) 428-8200
• Allen County Public Library
900 Webster Street
Fort Wayne, IN 46802
(219) 424-0544
Indiana University Northwest Library
3400 Broadway
Gary, IN 46408
(219) 980-6582
• Indianapolis-Marion County
Public Library
Social Sciences
40 E. St. Clair
Indianapolis, IN 46206
(317) 269-1733
Vigo County Public Library
One Liberty Square
Terre Haute, IN 47807
(812) 232-1113

Iowa
• Cedar Rapids Public Library
Foundation Center Collection
500 First Street, SE
Cedar Rapids, IA 52401
(319) 398-5123
• Southwestern Comm. College
Learning Resource Center
1501 W. Townline Road
Creston, IA 50801
(515) 782-7081

• Public Library of Des Moines
100 Locust
Des Moines, IA 50309
(515) 283-4152
• Sioux City Public Library
529 Pierce Street
Sioux City, IA 51101
(712) 252-5669

Kansas
• Dodge City Public Library
1001 2nd Avenue
Dodge City, KS 67801
(316) 225-0248
• Topeka and Shawnee County
Public Library
1515 SW 10th Avenue
Topeka, KS 66604
(913) 233-2040
• Wichita Public Library
223 S. Main Street
Wichita, KS 67202
(316) 262-0611

Kentucky
Western Kentucky University
Helm-Cravens Library
Bowling Green, KY 42101
(502) 745-6125
• Lexington Public Library
140 E. Main Street
Lexington, KY 40507
(606) 231-5520
• Louisville Free Public Library
301 York Street
Louisville, KY 40203
(502) 574-1611

Louisiana
• East Baton Rouge Parish Library
Centroplex Branch Grants Collection
120 St. Louis
Baton Rouge, LA 70802
(504) 389-4960
• Beauregard Parish Library
205 S. Washington Avenue
De Ridder, LA 70634
(318) 463-6217
Ouachita Parish Public Library
1800 Stubbs Avenue
Monroe, LA 71201
(318) 327-1490
• New Orleans Public Library
Business and Science Division
219 Loyola Avenue
New Orleans, LA 70140
(504) 596-2580

• Shreve Memorial Library
424 Texas Street
Shreveport, LA 71120
(318) 226-5894

Maine
• Maine Grants Information Center
University of Southern Maine Library
314 Forrest Ave.
Portland, ME 04104
(207) 780-5029

Maryland
• Enoch Pratt Free Library
Social Science and History
400 Cathedral Street
Baltimore, MD 21201
(410) 396-5430

Massachusetts
• Associated Grantmakers
of Massachusetts
294 Washington Street, Suite 840
Boston, MA 02108
(617) 426-2606
• Boston Public Library
Social Science Reference
700 Boylston Street
Boston, MA 02117
(617) 536-5400
Western Mass. Funding
Resource Center
65 Elliot Street
Springfield, MA 01101
(413) 732-3175
• Worcester Public Library
Grants Resource Center
Salem Square
Worcester, MA 01608
(508) 799-1655

Michigan
• Alpena County Library
211 N. First Street
Alpena, MI 49707
(517) 356-6188
• University of Michigan, Ann Arbor
Graduate Library
Reference & Research Services Dept.
Ann Arbor, MI 48109
(313) 764-9373
• Willard Public Library
7 W. Van Buren Street
Battle Creek, MI 49017
(616) 968-8166

• Henry Ford Centennial Library
Adult Services
16301 Michigan Avenue
Dearborn, MI 48126
(313) 943-2330
• Wayne State University
Purdy-Kresge Library
5265 Cass Avenue
Detroit, MI 48202
(313) 577-6424
• Michigan State University Libraries
Social Sciences/Humanities
Main Library
East Lansing, MI 48824
(517) 353-8818
• Farmington Comm. Library
32737 W. 12 Mile Road
Farmington Hills, MI 48018
(810) 553-0300
• University of Michigan, Flint
Library
Flint, MI 48502
(810) 762-3408
• Grand Rapids Public Library
Business Department, 3rd Floor
60 Library Plaza NE
Grand Rapids, MI 49503
(616) 456-3600
Michigan Technological University
Van Pelt Library
1400 Townsend Drive
Houghton, MI 49931
(906) 487-2507
Maud Preston Palenske Mem. Library
500 Market Street
Saint Joseph, MI 49085
(616) 983-7167
• Northwestern Michigan College
Mark & Helen Osterin Library
1701 E. Front Street
Traverse City, MI 49684
(616) 922-1060

Minnesota
• Duluth Public Library
520 W. Superior Street
Duluth, MN 55802
(218) 723-3802
• Southwest State University
University Library
Marshall, MN 56258
(507) 537-6176

• Minneapolis Public Library
Sociology Department
300 Nicollet Mall
Minneapolis, MN 55401
(612) 630-6300
Rochester Public Library
101 2nd Street, SE
Rochester, MN 55904
(507) 285-8002
St. Paul Public Library
90 W. Fourth Street
St. Paul, MN 55102
(612) 266-7000

Mississippi
• Jackson/Hinds Library System
300 N. State Street
Jackson, MS 39201
(601) 968-5803

Missouri
• Clearinghouse for
Midcontinent Foundations
University of Missouri
5110 Cherry, Suite 310
Kansas City, MO 64110
(816) 235-1176
• Kansas City Public Library
311 E. 12th Street
Kansas City, MO 64106
(816) 221-9650
• Metropolitan Association for
Philanthropy, Inc.
One Metropolitan Square, Suite 1295
211 North Broadway
St. Louis, MO 63102
(314) 621-6220
• Springfield-Greene Co. Library
397 E. Central
Springfield, MO 65802
(417) 837-5000

Montana
• Montana State University, Billings
Library-Special Collections
1500 N. 30th Street
Billings, MT 59101
(406) 657-1662
• Bozeman Public Library
220 E. Lamme
Bozeman, MT 59715
(406) 582-2402
• Montana State Library
Library Services
1515 E. 6th Avenue
Helena, MT 59620
(406) 444-3004

• University of Montana
Maureen & Mike Mansfield Library
Missoula, MT 59812
(406) 243-6800
Nebraska
• University of Nebraska, Lincoln
Love Library
14th and R Streets
Lincoln, NE 68588
(402) 472-2848
• W. Dale Clark Library
Social Sciences Department
215 S. 15th Street
Omaha, NE 68102
(402) 444-4826
Nevada
• Las Vegas-Clark County
Library District
1401 E. Flamingo
Las Vegas, NV 89119
(702) 733-3642
• Washoe County Library
301 S. Center Street
Reno, NV 89501
(702) 785-4010
New Hampshire
• Concord County Library
45 Green Street
Concord, NH 03301
(603) 225-8670
• Plymouth State College
Herbert H. Lamson Library
Plymouth, NH 03264
(603) 535-2258
New Jersey
Cumberland County Library
800 E. Commerce Street
Bridgeton, NJ 08302
(609) 453-2210
• Free Public Library of Elizabeth
11 S. Broad Street
Elizabeth, NJ 07202
(908) 354-6060
• County College of Morris
Learning Resource Center
214 Center Grove Road
Randolph, NJ 07869
(201) 328-5296
• New Jersey State Library
Governmental Reference Services
185 W. State Street
Trenton, NJ 08625
(609) 292-6220

New Mexico
• Albuquerque Community
Foundation
3301 Menual NE, Suite 30
Albuquerque, NM 87176
(505) 883-6240
• New Mexico State Library
Information Services
1209 Camino Carlos Rey
Santa Fe, NM 87505
(505) 476-9714
New York
• New York State Library
Humanities Reference
Cultural Education Center
Empire State Plaza
Albany, NY 12230
(518) 474-5355
Suffolk Cooperative Library System
627 N. Sunrise Service Road
Bellport, NY 11713
(516) 286-1600
New York Public Library
Bronx Reference Center
2556 Bainbridge Avenue
Bronx, NY 10458
(718) 579-4257
The Nonprofit Connection, Inc.
One Hanson Place, Room 2504
Brooklyn, NY 11243
(718) 230-3200
Brooklyn Public Library
Social Sciences Division
Grand Army Plaza
Brooklyn, NY 11238
(718) 780-7700
• Buffalo and Erie County
Public Library
Business and Labor Department
Lafayette Square
Buffalo, NY 14203
(716) 858-7097
Huntington Public Library
338 Main Street
Huntington, NY 11743
(516) 427-5165
Queens Borough Public Library
Social Sciences Division
89-11 Merrick Blvd.
Jamaica, NY 11432
(718) 990-8671
• Levittown Public Library
1 Bluegrass Lane
Levittown, NY 11756
(516) 731-5728

New York Public Library
Countee Cullen Branch Library
104 W. 136th Street
New York, NY 10030
(212) 491-2070
• The Foundation Center
79 Fifth Avenue, 2nd Floor
New York, NY 10003
(212) 620-4230
Adriance Memorial Library
Special Services Department
93 Market Street
Poughkeepsie, NY 12601
(914) 485-3445
• Rochester Public Library
Social Sciences
115 South Avenue
Rochester, NY 14604
(716) 428-8128
Onondaga Co. Public Library
447 S. Salina Street
Syracuse, NY 13202
(315) 435-1800
Utica Public Library
303 Genesee Street
Utica, NY 13501
(315) 735-2279
White Plains Public Library
100 Martine Avenue
White Plains, NY 10601
(914) 422-1480
North Carolina
• Community Foundation of
Western North Carolina
Learning Resources Center
16 Biltmore Avenue, Suite 201
P.O. Box 1888
Asheville, NC 28802
(704) 254-4960
• The Duke Endowment
100 N. Tryon Street, Suite 3500
Charlotte, NC 28202
(704) 376-0291
Durham County Public Library
301 N. Roxboro
Durham, NC 27702
(919) 560-0110
• State Library of North Carolina
Government and Business Services
Archives Building
109 E. Jones Street
Raleigh, NC 27601
(919) 733-3270

• Forsyth Co. Public Library
660 W. 5th Street
Winston-Salem, NC 27101
(336) 727-2680

North Dakota
• Bismarck Public Library
515 N. Fifth Street
Bismarck, ND 58501
(701) 222-6410
• Fargo Public Library
102 N. 3rd Street
Fargo, ND 58102
(701) 241-1491

Ohio
Stark County District Library
Humanities
715 Market Avenue North
Canton, OH 44702
(330) 452-0665
• Public Library of Cincinnati
and Hamilton County
Grants Resource Center
800 Vine Street-Library Square
Cincinnati, OH 45202
(513) 369-6940
• The Foundation Center
Kent H. Smith Library
1422 Euclid, Suite 1356
Cleveland, OH 44115
(216) 861-1933
Columbus Metro. Library
Business and Technology
96 S. Grant Ave.
Columbus, OH 43215
(614) 645-2590
• Dayton and Montgomery County
Public Library
Grants Resource Center
215 E. Third Street
Dayton, OH 45402
(937) 227-9500 ext. 211
• Mansfield/Richland County
Public Library
42 W. 3rd Street
Mansfield, OH 44902
(419) 521-3110
• Toledo-Lucas County
Public Library
Social Sciences Department
325 Michigan Street
Toledo, OH 43624
(419) 259-5245

• Public Library of Youngstown and
Mahoning County
305 Wick Avenue
Youngstown, OH 44503
(330) 744-8636
Muskingum County Library
220 N. 5th Street
Zanesville, OH 43701
(614) 453-0391

Oklahoma
• Oklahoma City University
Dulaney Browne Library
2501 N. Blackwelder
Oklahoma City, OK 73106
(405) 521-5822
• Tulsa City-County Library
400 Civic Center
Tulsa, OK 74103
(918) 596-7944

Oregon
Oregon Inst. of Technology Library
3201 Campus Drive
Klamath Falls, OR 97601
(503) 885-1773
• Pacific Non-Profit Network
Grantsmanship Resource Library
33 N. Central, Suite 211
Medford, OR 97501
(503) 779-6044
Multnomah County Library
Government Documents
801 SW Tenth Avenue
Portland, OR 97205
(503) 248-5123
• Oregon State Library
State Library Building
Salem, OR 97310
(503) 378-4277

Pennsylvania
Northampton Community College
Learning Resources Center
3835 Green Pond Road
Bethlehem, PA 18017
(610) 861-5360
Erie County Library System
160 E. Front Street
Erie, PA 16507
(814) 451-6927
Dauphin County Library System
Central Library
101 Walnut Street
Harrisburg, PA 17101
(717) 234-4976

Lancaster County Public Library
125 N. Duke Street
Lancaster, PA 17602
(717) 394-2651
• Free Library of Philadelphia
Regional Foundation Center
Logan Square
Philadelphia, PA 19103
(215) 686-5423
• Carnegie Library of Pittsburgh
Foundation Collection
4400 Forbes Avenue
Pittsburgh, PA 15213
(412) 622-1917
Pocono Northeast Development Fund
James Pettinger Memorial Library
1151 Oak Street
Pittston, PA 18640
(717) 655-5581
Reading Public Library
100 S. Fifth Street
Reading, PA 19602
(610) 655-6355
• Martin Library
159 Market Street
York, PA 17401
(717) 846-5300

Rhode Island
• Providence Public Library
225 Washington Street
Providence, RI 02906
(401) 455-8088

South Carolina
• Anderson County Library
202 E. Greenville Street
Anderson, SC 29621
(864) 260-4500
• Charleston County Library
68 Calhoun Street
Charleston, SC 29401
(843) 805-6950
• South Carolina State Library
1500 Senate Street
Columbia, SC 29211
(803) 734-8666
Community Foundation of
Greater Greenville
27 Cleveland Street, Suite 101
P.O. Box 6909
Greenville, SC 29606
(864) 233-5925

South Dakota

• South Dakota State Library
800 Governors Drive
Pierre, SD 57501
(605) 773-5070
(800) 592-1841 (SD residents)
Nonprofit Management Institute
132 S. Dakota Road
Sioux Falls, SD 57102
(605) 367-5380
• Siouxland Libraries
201 N. Main Avenue
Sioux Falls, SD 57104
(605) 367-7081

Tennessee

• Knox County Public Library
500 W. Church Avenue
Knoxville, TN 37902
(423) 544-5700
• Memphis & Shelby County
Public Library
1850 Peabody Avenue
Memphis, TN 38104
(901) 725-8877
• Nashville Public Library
Business Information Division
225 Polk Avenue
Nashville, TN 37203
(615) 862-5843

Texas

Nonprofit Resource Center
Funding Information Library
500 N. Chestnut, Suite 1511
Abilene, TX 79604
(915) 677-8166
• Amarillo Area Foundation
700 First National Place
801 S. Fillmore
Amarillo, TX 79101
(806) 376-4521
• Hogg Foundation for
Mental Health
3001 Lake Austin Blvd.
Austin, TX 78703
(512) 471-5041
Beaumont Public Library
801 Pearl Street
Beaumont, TX 77704
(409) 838-6606
Corpus Christi Public Library
805 Comanche Street
Reference Department
Corpus Christi, TX 78401
(512) 880-7000

• Dallas Public Library
Urban Information
1515 Young Street
Dallas, TX 75201
(214) 670-1487
Southwest Border Nonprofit
Resource Center
Nonprofit Resource Center
1201 W. University Drive
Edinburgh, TX 78539
(956) 316-2610
Center for Volunteerism and
Nonprofit Management
1918 Texas Avenue
El Paso, TX 79901
(915) 532-5377
• Funding Information Center of
Fort Worth
329 S. Henderson
Ft. Worth, TX 76104
(817) 334-0228
• Houston Public Library
Bibliographic Information Center
500 McKinney
Houston, TX 77002
(713) 236-1313
Nonprofit Management and
Volunteer Center
Laredo Public Library
1120 East Calton Road
Laredo, TX 78041
(956) 795-2400
• Longview Public Library
222 W. Cotton Street
Longview, TX 75601
(903) 237-1352
Lubbock Area Foundation, Inc.
1655 Main Street, Suite 209
Lubbock, TX 79401
(806) 762-8061
• Nonprofit Resource Center of Texas
111 Soledad, Suite 200
San Antonio, TX 78205
(210) 227-4333
Waco-McLennan County Library
1717 Austin Avenue
Waco, TX 76701
(254) 750-5975
• North Texas Center for
Nonprofit Management
624 Indiana, Suite 307
Wichita Falls, TX 76301
(940) 322-4961

Utah

• Salt Lake City Public Library
209 E. 500 South
Salt Lake City, UT 84111
(801) 524-8200

Vermont

• Vermont Department of Libraries
Reference & Law Info. Services
109 State Street
Montpelier, VT 05609
(802) 828-3268

Virginia

Hampton Public Library
4207 Victoria Blvd.
Hampton, VA 23669
(757) 727-1312
• Richmond Public Library
Business, Science & Technology
101 E. Franklin Street
Richmond, VA 23219
(804) 780-8223
• Roanoke City Public
Library System
706 S. Jefferson Street
Roanoke, VA 24016
(540) 853-2477

Washington

• Mid-Columbia Library
405 S. Dayton
Kennewick, WA 99336
(509) 586-3156
• Seattle Public Library
Science, Social Science
1000 Fourth Avenue
Seattle, WA 98104
(206) 386-4620
• Spokane Public Library
Funding Information Center
West 811 Main Avenue
Spokane, WA 99201
(509) 626-5347
• United Way of Pierce County
Center for Nonprofit Development
1501 Pacific Avenue, Suite 400
P.O. Box 2215
Tacoma, WA 98401
(206) 272-4263
Greater Wenatchee Community
Foundation at the Wenatchee
Public Library
310 Douglas Street
Wenatchee, WA 98807
(509) 662-5021

West Virginia
• Kanawha County Public Library
123 Capitol Street
Charleston, WV 25301
(304) 343-4646

Wisconsin
• University of Wisconsin, Madison
Memorial Library
728 State Street
Madison, WI 53706
(608) 262-3242
• Marquette University
Memorial Library
Funding Information Center
1415 W. Wisconsin Avenue
Milwaukee, WI 53201
(414) 288-1515
• University of Wisconsin,
Stevens Point
Library-Foundation Collection
99 Reserve Street
Stevens Point, WI 54481
(715) 346-4204

Wyoming
• Natrona County Public Library
307 East 2nd Street
Casper, WY 82601
(307) 237-4935
• Laramie Co. Community College
Instructional Resource Center
1400 E. College Drive
Cheyenne, WY 82007
(307) 778-1206
• Campbell County Public Library
2101 4-J Road
Gillette, WY 82716
(307) 682-3223
• Teton County Library
125 Virginia Lane
Jackson, WY 83001
(307) 733-2164
Rock Springs Library
400 C Street
Rock Springs, WY 82901
(307) 352-6667

Puerto Rico
Universidad Del Sagrado
Corazon
M.M.T. Guevara Library
Santurce, PR 00914
(809) 728-1515 ext. 4357

Appendix B

The Grantsmanship Center

The Grantsmanship Center is the world's oldest and largest training organization for the nonprofit sector. Since it was founded in 1972, the Center has trained more than 65,000 staff members of public and private agencies in grantsmanship, program management and fundraising.

The five-day *Grantsmanship Training Program*, first offered in 1972 and continuously updated, began a new era in training seminars and workshops for nonprofit agencies. Over 35,000 nonprofit agency staff members have attended this demanding, week-long workshop, the single most widely attended training program in the history of the nonprofit sector. It covers all aspects of researching for grants, writing grant proposals, and negotiating with funding sources.

The *Grant Proposal Writing Workshop*, an intensive three-day laboratory, teaches you how to write a good proposal and plan better programs at the same time, using the Grantsmanship Center's program planning and proposal writing format.

The five-day *Strategic Fundraising Workshop*, launched in 1996, teaches you how to develop a comprehensive fundraising strategy to keep your organization strong. Like other Grantsmanship Center training programs, it combines structured analysis, focused discussions, and small-group exercises and limits class size to 25 participants.

The Center also produces publications on grantsmanship, planning, fundraising, management, and personnel issues for nonprofit agencies. Its *Program Planning and Proposal Writing* booklet is now a classic in the field and has been used by hundreds of thousands of successful grant seekers.

For detailed information about The Grantsmanship Center's training programs, publications, and other services to the nonprofit sector, write to The Grantsmanship Center, Dept. DD, P.O. Box 17220, Los Angeles, CA 90017 and ask for a free copy of *The Grantsmanship Center Magazine*.

Index to Foundations

(Alphabetical)

Citations are by entry number

D

H

I

M

Mabee (J.E. and L.E.) Foundation, Inc., 562

MacArthur (John D. and Catherine T.) Foundation, 239

MacLean Foundation, Inc., 293

Macy, Jr. (Josiah) Foundation, 486

Maddox (J.F) Foundation, 445

Madison Community Foundation, 716

Magale Foundation, Inc., 301

Magee-O'Connor Foundation, Inc., 273

Mardag Foundation, 387

Margaret Hall Foundation, Inc., 294

Margoes Foundation, 79

Marshall Fund of Arizona, 14

Marshall (George Preston) Foundation, 318

Massey Charitable Trust, 594

Mayerson (Manuel D. & Rhoda) Foundation, 538

Maytag (Fred) Family Foundation, 279

Mazza Foundation, 240

McArthur (J.N.) Foundation, Inc., 184

McBeath (Faye) Foundation, 717

McCabe (B.C.) Foundation, 80

McConnell Foundation, 81

McCormick (Robert R.) Tribune Foundation, 241

McCune Charitable Foundation, 446

McCune Foundation, 595

McDonald Family Trust, 149

McDonough (Bernard) Foundation, Inc., 709

McElroy (R.J.) Trust, 280

McGraw (Curtis W.) Foundation, 434

McGregor Fund, 363

McInerny Foundation, 216

MCJ Foundation, 435

McKee (Robert E. and Evelyn) Foundation, 661

McKenna (Katherine Mabis) Foundation, Inc., 596

McKessonHBOC Foundation, Inc., 82

McKnight Foundation, 388

McShain (John) Charities, Inc., 597

McWane Foundation, 6

Meadows Foundation, Inc., 662

Medina Foundation, 703

Medtronic Foundation, 389

Mellon Financial Corporation Foundation, 598

Mellon (Richard King) Foundation, 599

Memorial Foundation for Children, 690

Merrill Lynch & Company Foundation, Inc., 487

Metropolitan Life Foundation, 488

Meyer (Eugene and Agnes E.) Foundation, 167

Meyer Memorial Trust, 572

Meyer (Paul J.) Family Foundation, 663

Meyer (Robert R.) Foundation, 7

Mid-Iowa Health Foundation, 281

Mid-Nebraska Community Foundation, Inc., 415

Milken Family Foundation, 83

Monfort Family Foundation, 136

Montana Power Foundation, Inc., 408

Montgomery Street Foundation, 84

Moody Foundation, 664

Moores (Harry C.) Foundation, 539

Morgan (Burton D.) Foundation, 540

Morgan Stanley Dean Witter Foundation, 489

Morris (Margaret T.) Foundation, 15

Morrison (Harry W.) Foundation, Inc., 223

Murdock (M.J.) Charitable Trust, 704

Murphy (John P.) Foundation, 541

N

Nalco Foundation, 242

Nationwide Foundation, 542

NEC Foundation of America, 490

New York Times Company Foundation, Inc., 491

Nielsen (Aksel) Foundation, 137

Noble (Samuel Roberts) Foundation, Inc., 563

Norcliffe Foundation, 705

Nord Family Foundation, 543

Nordson Corporation Foundation, 544

Norfolk Foundation, 691

Norfolk Southern Foundation, 692

Norris (Kenneth T. and Eileen L.) Foundation, 85

North Family Trust, 617

Northern New York Community Foundation, 492

Index to Foundations

(Subject Index)

Citations are by entry number

EDUCATION—1, 11, 17, 18, 21, 27, 30, 32, 34, 40, 41, 44, 54, 56, 58, 62, 64, 66, 68, 70, 71, 84, 86, 88, 91, 92, 95, 96, 100, 101, 105, 111, 112, 116, 118, 120, 121, 124, 125, 126, 128, 129, 132, 134, 135, 140, 141, 142, 143, 144, 145, 146, 148, 150, 152, 156, 157, 160, 162, 163, 164, 167, 169, 173, 174, 175, 180, 188, 190, 195, 198, 203, 205, 209, 212, 213, 215, 216, 221, 224, 228, 229, 234, 235, 238, 242, 244, 246, 248, 255, 263, 267, 269, 275, 281, 287, 289, 294, 295, 299, 305, 308, 323, 324, 327, 328, 339, 341, 342, 345, 346, 351, 357, 362, 363, 366, 368, 370, 372, 374, 376, 377, 380, 382, 387, 388, 389, 394, 395, 399, 404, 407, 408, 411, 418, 419, 430, 436, 438, 439, 440, 441, 447, 448, 450, 452, 453, 456, 457, 461, 462, 464, 465, 467, 481, 483, 485, 486, 488, 490, 491, 493, 495, 497, 503, 507, 509, 515, 516, 517, 522, 524, 527, 529, 532, 533, 536, 538, 543, 544, 549, 552, 553, 556, 569, 572, 574, 577, 578, 579, 581, 582, 583, 585, 586, 587, 588, 589, 590, 591, 594, 600, 602, 606, 609, 610, 613, 618, 619, 626, 632, 634, 640, 642, 651, 655, 659, 662, 664, 669, 670, 675, 676, 681, 702, 704, 708, 714, 724

ELDERLY/ADULTS—2, 3, 14, 39, 40, 44, 47, 53, 54, 62, 63, 68, 70, 71, 88, 92, 105, 115, 118, 122, 123, 126, 132, 156, 160, 162, 171, 176, 178, 199, 228, 229, 231, 236, 238, 241, 248, 281, 303, 305, 321, 324, 327, 358, 374, 400, 416, 449, 489, 497, 499, 500, 507, 515, 519, 553, 577, 600, 634, 646, 662, 664, 689, 697, 712, 716

INDEPENDENT LIVING PROGRAMS—3, 24, 31, 36, 39, 43, 54, 60, 71, 88, 90, 92, 105, 107, 115, 126, 162, 171, 176, 183, 207, 211, 215, 216, 220, 230, 234, 236, 243, 246, 248, 306, 324, 325, 327, 348, 359, 374, 387, 391, 394, 443, 448, 480, 509, 519, 522, 525, 532, 549, 552, 614, 624, 627, 660, 677, 679, 691, 714, 720, 727

LEARNING DISABILITIES—11, 17, 62, 66, 70, 71, 84, 89, 91, 95, 105, 114, 118, 126, 131, 132, 140, 142, 144, 149, 150, 157, 161, 162, 163, 169, 174, 194, 212, 213, 215, 216, 220, 228, 229, 242, 243, 244, 253, 260, 267, 289, 293, 294, 299, 310, 321, 324, 327, 341, 343, 345, 346, 347, 351, 357, 362, 366, 370, 374, 376, 377, 382, 388, 394, 395, 399, 404, 419, 434, 441, 456, 462, 464, 491, 493, 495, 497, 509, 529, 530, 532, 544, 569, 572, 574, 577, 579, 588, 589, 600, 602, 612, 618, 619, 622, 634, 640, 655, 662, 664, 668, 676, 677, 688, 695, 714, 722, 724

MENTAL HEALTH—3, 4, 5, 6, 7, 9, 13, 17, 24, 25, 27, 31, 32, 36, 39, 40, 44, 61, 62, 63, 70, 79, 86, 88, 91, 92, 95, 96, 97, 98, 99, 101, 104, 109, 112, 115, 118, 119, 122, 124, 126, 138, 140, 143, 145, 155, 159, 160, 161, 162, 163, 165, 166, 167, 169, 170, 173, 175, 176, 179, 182, 183, 191, 195, 197, 200, 207, 210, 212, 214, 215, 216, 219, 220, 221, 227, 229, 230, 234, 236, 239, 241, 243, 247, 248, 263, 264, 268, 269, 280, 286, 287, 290, 294, 302, 305, 306, 308, 311, 313, 314, 319, 327, 328, 329, 336, 338, 341, 345, 353, 363, 365, 366, 368, 370, 372, 374, 378, 381, 382, 385, 387, 388, 389, 390, 391, 393, 394, 399, 401, 402, 408, 410, 416, 419, 425, 427, 430, 431, 434, 437, 440, 441, 446, 449, 450, 456, 460, 463, 465, 467, 468, 472, 473, 474, 476, 480, 497, 499, 504, 505, 507, 510, 515, 526, 532, 540, 542, 543, 544, 545, 547, 553, 563, 565, 566, 568, 572, 573, 574, 577, 583, 587, 592, 593, 597, 599, 600, 602, 603, 605, 609, 618, 622, 623, 628, 629, 638, 640, 643, 645, 647, 654, 655, 658, 660, 662, 667, 668, 671, 674, 677, 679, 681, 683, 686, 692, 693, 696, 698, 703, 708, 714, 719, 722, 726

MENTALLY DISABLED—1, 2, 3, 5, 7, 10, 11, 14, 16, 17, 18, 28, 31, 36, 38, 41, 43, 44, 54, 57, 64, 70, 74, 75, 78, 82, 89, 97, 105, 109, 113, 114, 115, 126, 132, 139, 143, 144, 145, 146, 154, 155, 156, 157, 158, 162, 165, 169, 171, 176, 177, 180, 181, 182, 183, 188, 190, 200, 206, 209, 213, 214, 216, 217, 220, 223, 226, 229, 241, 242, 243, 246, 249, 251, 253, 255, 256, 257, 258, 261, 263, 271, 272, 274, 278, 279, 280, 288, 289, 291, 292, 295, 296, 297, 298, 299, 301, 306, 308, 309, 311, 317, 318, 321, 327, 328, 338, 357, 360, 362, 372, 374, 376, 378, 382, 383, 392, 393, 395, 397, 398, 401, 403, 407, 408, 413, 420, 421, 423, 429, 430, 431, 435, 440, 442, 444, 445, 447, 449, 450, 452, 462, 466, 472, 477, 478, 480, 481, 482, 488, 489, 495, 497, 504, 505, 507, 508, 509, 510, 512, 513, 514, 515, 517, 522, 526, 527,

528, 531, 532, 536, 539, 542, 543, 545, 552, 555, 563, 564, 571, 573, 575, 577, 580, 581, 583, 584, 587, 588, 592, 594, 598, 599, 600, 602, 604, 605, 608, 610, 611, 614, 616, 620, 622, 629, 634, 635, 637, 644, 646, 647, 648, 653, 654, 655, 656, 658, 661, 662, 666, 667, 668, 672, 675, 677, 678, 681, 684, 687, 689, 690, 694, 696, 699, 700, 704, 706, 708, 709, 710, 715, 718, 720, 722, 723, 725

PHYSICALLY DISABLED—2, 3, 7, 9, 10, 11, 13, 15, 17, 18, 19, 20, 21, 22, 23, 28, 29, 31, 33, 36, 37, 38, 41, 42, 45, 47, 48, 49, 52, 53, 54, 55, 58, 60, 61, 63, 64, 65, 67, 68, 70, 72, 73, 75, 76, 77, 78, 79, 81, 82, 83, 84, 85, 87, 90, 91, 93, 94, 97, 98, 99, 102, 104, 105, 106, 107, 108, 110, 111, 113, 114, 115, 117, 118, 119, 122, 123, 126, 127, 128, 129, 130, 131, 132, 133, 134, 135, 136, 137, 138, 141, 142, 145, 146, 147, 151, 153, 155, 157, 159, 160, 162, 163, 166, 167, 170, 171, 172, 175, 176, 177, 179, 180, 181, 184, 185, 186, 187, 189, 191, 192, 193, 194, 196, 197, 198, 199, 203, 204, 205, 206, 208, 209, 210, 211, 214, 216, 217, 218, 219, 221, 222, 224, 225, 226, 227, 228, 229, 230, 233, 234, 235, 236, 238, 240, 241, 242, 244, 245, 247, 249, 251, 252, 253, 255, 256, 259, 263, 264, 265, 266, 267, 268, 270, 271, 272, 273, 274, 275, 277, 278, 279, 280, 281, 282, 283, 285, 286, 288, 291, 292, 295, 298, 300, 303, 304, 305, 307, 308, 309, 310, 313, 315, 316, 317, 318, 320, 322, 326, 328, 329, 331, 333, 335, 336, 337, 338, 341, 343, 347, 350, 351, 353, 355, 356, 357, 358, 359, 360, 361, 364, 366, 367, 373, 374, 377, 378, 379, 380, 381, 382, 384, 385, 386, 390, 391, 393, 394, 395, 396, 398, 399, 400, 401, 402, 403, 405, 406, 409, 410, 411, 413, 414, 415, 420, 422, 423, 424, 426, 430, 431, 432, 433, 434, 435, 436, 439, 440, 442, 445, 446, 447, 448, 450, 451, 453, 454, 455, 456, 458, 459, 461, 462, 463, 465, 469, 470, 471, 472, 474, 475, 477, 479, 482, 483, 484, 487, 489, 490, 491, 492, 495, 496, 498, 501, 502, 503, 504, 505, 506, 507, 509, 510, 511, 513, 515, 516, 518, 519, 520, 522, 523, 524, 525, 526, 527, 528, 531, 532, 533, 535, 536, 538, 539, 541, 542, 544, 546, 547, 548, 550, 552, 553, 555, 558, 560, 561, 562, 563, 564, 565, 567, 568, 569, 571, 572, 573, 574, 575, 576, 577, 579, 583, 584, 586, 589, 590, 591, 592, 594, 595, 597, 598, 599, 600, 601, 602, 603, 604, 606, 607, 608, 610, 611, 612, 613, 615, 617, 620, 623, 624, 625, 626, 627, 628, 629, 632, 633, 634, 636, 637, 638, 641, 643, 644, 645, 646, 647, 648, 649, 650, 651, 652, 653, 654, 656, 657, 658, 660, 662, 663, 664, 666, 667, 669, 671, 673, 675, 679, 681, 682, 684, 686, 687, 689, 690, 691, 693, 694, 695, 696, 697, 698, 699, 700, 702, 703, 704, 705, 707, 708, 709, 710, 711, 712, 714, 715, 717, 718, 720, 721, 722, 723, 724, 725

RECREATION—3, 10, 11, 16, 17, 28, 39, 40, 41, 43, 54, 57, 64, 77, 78, 82, 84, 88, 89, 96, 105, 109, 113, 114, 115, 116, 117, 118, 119, 121, 125, 126, 128, 130, 131, 132, 136, 137, 141, 143, 144, 145, 154, 162, 176, 177, 178, 180, 183, 185, 191, 194, 200, 205, 209, 213, 220, 223, 229, 234, 238, 241, 242, 243, 246, 251, 256, 257, 258, 259, 261, 264, 266, 269, 271, 280, 288, 292, 296, 301, 305, 306, 309, 314, 317, 328, 342, 345, 357, 373, 376, 377, 378, 380, 382, 383, 385, 392, 395, 397, 401, 407, 408, 409, 411, 423, 428, 430, 442, 444, 447, 461, 462, 464, 466, 467, 488, 509, 510, 512, 515, 519, 520, 521, 524, 527, 529, 532, 536, 541, 545, 546, 547, 549, 563, 564, 573, 580, 581, 589, 592, 600, 614, 620, 621, 647, 652, 658, 661, 662, 664, 666, 670, 675, 681, 684, 687, 689, 693, 694, 696, 697, 699, 700, 704, 706, 708, 709, 714, 720, 722, 723, 724

SPEECH IMPAIRED—61, 66, 87, 91, 100, 115, 119, 126, 170, 180, 193, 199, 203, 205, 206, 215, 305, 345, 347, 377, 382, 390, 394, 433, 463, 482, 493, 497, 520, 521, 523, 527, 537, 538, 544, 550, 558, 559, 560, 561, 567, 569, 573, 650, 655, 668, 697

VOCATIONAL TRAINING/EMPLOYMENT PROJECTS—11, 30, 39, 49, 50, 52, 55, 56, 67, 75, 76, 86, 92, 102, 103, 117, 121, 126, 128, 133, 135, 147, 156, 160, 162, 166, 167, 181, 182, 183, 187, 201, 208, 210, 212, 214, 216, 217, 219, 221, 229, 230, 231, 232, 239, 242, 250, 254, 277, 283, 285, 299, 306, 312, 313, 318, 328, 329, 330, 346, 350, 354, 355, 371, 374, 380, 396, 434, 435, 447, 453, 459, 481, 507, 509, 522, 525, 529, 530, 537, 539, 542, 543, 556, 562, 568, 572, 581, 583, 584, 587, 588, 593, 598, 600, 603, 612, 620, 633, 634, 636, 639, 646, 655, 657, 658, 662, 666, 667, 672, 677, 707, 719

YOUTH—2, 3, 17, 21, 25, 30, 32, 33, 34, 35, 36, 38, 39, 40, 41, 44, 45, 54, 55, 62, 63, 66, 68, 70, 71, 76, 79, 85, 86, 88, 91, 92, 94, 96, 99, 100, 101, 104, 105, 108, 111, 112, 113, 115, 116, 117, 118, 119, 124, 126, 128, 131, 132, 133, 141, 143, 144, 153, 156, 158, 160, 162, 173, 176, 178, 179, 180, 182, 183, 190, 191, 205, 211, 212, 213, 215, 216, 217, 222, 228, 229, 233, 234, 235, 238, 241, 242, 243, 246, 247, 249, 261, 264, 265, 274, 278, 280, 281, 286, 289, 295, 299, 302, 303, 305, 307, 308, 309, 318, 320, 324, 325, 327, 328, 331, 336, 338, 341, 342, 344, 345, 347, 351, 353, 358, 360, 362, 363, 365, 367, 372, 375, 377, 380, 384, 386, 387, 388, 390, 391, 394, 399, 400, 402, 404, 405, 408, 411, 413, 415, 416, 418, 419, 422, 428, 430, 438, 439, 440, 441, 446, 448, 450, 453, 456, 457, 460, 461, 462, 465, 468, 470, 471, 472, 474, 475, 476, 481, 483, 484, 486, 488, 489, 491, 493, 495, 496, 497, 498, 499, 504, 507, 511, 517, 524, 527, 528, 532, 547, 548, 549, 553, 556, 569, 572, 573, 574, 577, 581, 583, 584, 586, 587, 588, 589, 590, 592, 594, 595, 597, 600, 601, 602, 606, 607, 608, 610, 613, 614, 618, 622, 630, 634, 640, 642, 645, 647, 650, 653, 654, 659, 662, 664, 666, 669, 671, 675, 677, 679, 681, 690, 691, 697, 700, 701, 702, 704, 714, 715, 717, 719, 722, 723, 724, 725

Research Grant Guides, Inc.

We publish these fund-raising Directories:

Directory of Health Grants
Directory of Program Grants
Directory of Operating Grants
Directory of Social Service Grants
Directory of Building and Equipment Grants
Directory of Computer and High Technology Grants
Directory of Grants for Organizations Serving People with Disabilities

To request our current sales brochure, please mail or fax this request form to:

Research Grant Guides, Inc.
Dept. 4A
P.O. Box 1214
Loxahatchee, FL 33470
Fax (561) 795-7794

Name _____

Title _____

Organization _____

Address _____

City_____State_____Zip_____